ON THE AIR

ON THE AIR

FIFTEEN PLAYS FOR
BROADCAST AND FOR CLASSROOM USE

COLLECTED AND EDITED BY

GARRETT H. LEVERTON

SAMUEL FRENCH

New York   *Toronto*   *Los Angeles*

SAMUEL FRENCH Ltd., London

1947

MANUFACTURED IN THE UNITED STATES OF AMERICA
BY THE VAIL-BALLOU PRESS, INC., BINGHAMTON, N. Y.

CONTENTS

NOT AVAILABLE FOR BROADCAST

80%..

60%

Good

all girls

MAY 11 1949

A YOUNG MAN'S FANCY

By

HILDA MANNING

CAST

MRS. HUNTER
MR. HUNTER
MARJORIE
DONNIE
BERT
JANIE MILLER

A YOUNG MAN'S FANCY

(*MUSIC: Theme music up and fade under for:*)

ANNOUNCER. Presenting—*A Young Man's Fancy,* a play for radio by Hilda Manning.

(*MUSIC: Up for five seconds and then under.*)

ANNOUNCER. The scene of our play is Middleville, a typical American small town. Here in Middleville the family is the important thing and everything revolves around it. On a quiet, peaceful street stands the comfortable home of the Hunter family. It is soon after dinner on a warm Spring night and the town is quiet. But inside the Hunter home it is far from quiet, in fact, there is quite a commotion going on. As we listen we hear—

(*FADE OUT as the music fades in.*)

(*MUSIC: The musical background should be some light piece of springtime and young love, such as Mendelssohn's "Spring Song." It plays for a few seconds and then fades out after the introductory strains.*)

(*FADE IN: Girl's footsteps running down a carpeted hall.*)

MARJORIE (*off mike, calling*). Mother!

MOTHER (*on mike, answering*). Yes, Marjorie?

MARJORIE (*off mike*). Where are you?

MOTHER. Here in my room, dear.

MARJORIE (*fading on mike*). Mother, I would merely like to know how much longer he's going to be in there, that's all.

MOTHER. Who's going to be in where?

MARJORIE (*on mike*). It's simply outrageous, that's what it is—

3

monopolizing the bathroom that way. I'm ages late as it is, and I haven't even bathed yet—

MOTHER. Is Donnie in there again?

MARJORIE. No, Mother, he's not in there again. He's in there *yet!* And it's nearly eight right now!

MOTHET. Heavens! (*Fading off mike*) I'll see what's keeping him. (*Off mike, calling*) Donnie, how much longer are you—?

DONNIE (*off mike, calling, voice muffled by door*). Keep your shirt on, Mom! I'll be right out.

MARJORIE. He's been saying that for an hour. And if Everett calls for me and I'm late, *you* can just explain to him why, Mother.

MOTHER (*fading on mike*). Now, Marjorie—

MARJORIE. You can explain to him that, as far as my younger brother is concerned, it's entirely immaterial whether or not I ever take another bath. You can—

MOTHER. Now, that's enough, Marjorie. You're always late, anyway. Besides, isn't this the night of Donnie's "Freshman Hop," or whatever you call it?

MARJORIE. I should think you'd put your foot down about that, Mother, I honestly do. A boy of *his* age—having *dates!*

MOTHER. After all, it's only his first one. And when it comes to the matter of age, young lady, you aren't exactly Mrs. Methuselah yourself.

MARJORIE. I'm different. I'm entirely able to take care of myself. But a *mere* boy of *fifteen*—

MOTHER. Donnie was sixteen last month.

MARJORIE. Don't quibble, Mother!

(SOUND: *Man's footsteps approaching.*)

BERT (*fading on mike*). Hello! Why the pow-wow?

MOTHER. Oh, it's nothing, Bert! Marjorie's just upset, that's all.

A YOUNG MAN'S FANCY

MARJORIE. I should say I am! And where do you think you're going in your bathrobe, Bert?

BERT. Me? Just going to soak the old torso. Why?

MARJORIE. Oh, no, you're not!

BERT. Who says not?

MARJORIE. That darling little brother of ours is having himself a private water carnival in the bathtub.

BERT. Donnie's not actually taking a *bath!*

MARJORIE. So he claims.

BERT. In the middle of the week? What's up?

MOTHER. He's going to that Freshman thing they're having to-night.

MARJORIE. With a *girl*, if you please!

BERT (*laughs*). No!

MOTHER. And where are you going this evening, Bert?

BERT. Oh, no place much, Mother. Mildred and I are driving over to Wildwood. And if I don't get under that shower quick I'm going to be late again. And Mildred says the next time will be the last.

MARJORIE. You'll just have to wait your turn. (*Calls*) For heaven's sake, Donnie, hurry up!

DONNIE (*off mike, calling*). Okay!

(*FADE OUT.*)

(*MUSIC: Fade theme music up for five seconds and then under.*)

(*FADE IN.*)

DONNIE (*off mike, behind closed door*). Hey, Mom!

MOTHER (*fading on mike*). What is it, Donnie?

(*SOUND: Footsteps, door opens.*)

MOTHER. Yes, Donnie?

DONNIE (*on mike*). Mom, did you ask Dad if I could have the coupé tonight? Did you?

5

MOTHER. Donnie, this room of yours is a fright! And what in the world are you doing with that hat?

DONNIE. This hat? Aw, I'm just wearing it, Mom.

MOTHER. I can see that. But why?

DONNIE. Oh, for gosh sakes! Well, if you must know, it's just merely to kind of keep my hair in place.

MOTHER. What's the matter, are you afraid of losing it? Your hair, I mean?

DONNIE. That's not the point at all, Mom. The point is that if I don't wanna look like some wild man, or something, I gotta wear the hat to make my hair lay down. You wouldn't want your own son to be seen in public looking like a wild man or something, would you, Mom?

MOTHER (*chuckles*). No, I suppose not.

DONNIE. Okay! Did you ask him, Mom? Did you?

MOTHER. Did I ask whom what?

DONNIE. Well, holy gosh, I just told you! Don't you ever listen to *anything* I say? Did you ask Dad if I could have the coupé?

MOTHER. No, I did not. And what's more, I'm not going to. Wednesday is the one night in the week your father wants the coupé himself.

DONNIE. What for? A mere, unimportant little old thing like a measly old Lodge meeting!

MOTHER. Lodge meetings *aren't* unimportant to your father.

DONNIE. That's just about the most unreasonable thing I ever heard, Mom, it honestly is! I don't make any demands on this family—not half as many as some people I could mention. And when I do happen to ask for a measly little favor like having the coupé to attend a very important and unusual function, you start telling me about silly old Lodge meetings. Just put yourself in my place, Mom. All I wanna know is, do you think it's *fair?*

6

MOTHER. Oh, stop raving, child. If your father chooses to let you have the coupé, I'm willing. But you'll have to ask him yourself. He's downstairs in the living room.

DONNIE. That's fine, that is! That's gratitude, that is.
"My heart aches, and a drowsy numbness pains
My sense, as though of hemlock I had drunk—"

MOTHER. For heaven's sake, what's that?

DONNIE. Keats; he suffered, too.

MOTHER. Well, sufferer, don't you think you'd better get dressed now?

DONNIE. Holy gosh, I certainly do! Why didn't you tell me it was so late? Hey, Mom, will you kind of tie this tie for me?

MOTHER. Stand still then.

DONNIE. These collars are getting awful tight on me. Better buy them half a size larger next time.

MOTHER. All right, Donnie.

DONNIE. Guess I've just about attained my full growth, practically.

MOTHER. Dear me! It seems such a little while ago that I was tucking you in your crib every night.

DONNIE. Aw, Mom, is that any way to talk to a grown man?

MOTHER (*amused*). I suppose not.

DONNIE. If you don't believe I'm a man, just take a look at my chin.

MOTHER. What is it, a spot of dirt? Wait a minute, I'll wipe it off.

DONNIE. You can't rub it off, Mom—

MOTHER. Why not?

DONNIE. Because it's *hair,* that's what it is!

MOTHER. Is it!

DONNIE. You seem to kind of forget, Mom, that I'm practically seventeen now.

MOTHER. You were sixteen last month.

DONNIE. Well, for gosh sakes, Mom, I haven't got time to argue with you. Isn't that tie fixed yet?

MOTHER. Stand still.

DONNIE.   "She walks in beauty, like the night
                    Of cloudless climes and starry skies—"

MOTHER. Can't you be quiet? I'll never get your tie tied.

DONNIE. Aw, I guess you just don't have any poetic appreciation, Mom.

MOTHER. Was that Keats again?

DONNIE. Byron. Good gosh, can't you even tell the difference between Keats and Byron? (*Dreamily*) I only wish I could write like that.

MOTHER. Why?

DONNIE. *Why?* Because then I'd probably be one of the most famous poets in the whole world practically, that's why. I guess *that* would make this family realize that I was a grown up man, instead of some little old schoolboy for everyone to pick on.

MOTHER. All right, your tie's tied now.

DONNIE. Gee, thanks, Mom. I guess a man's years don't really mean a great deal, do they, Mom? It all depends on how old his *soul* is.

MOTHER. What do you mean?

DONNIE. Now you just take me, for instance—

MOTHER. Yes?

DONNIE. Well, what I mean is, I feel a lot older, really, than most of the kids my age. I'm kind of interested in intellectual pursuits like poetry and—and things. I guess that sort of sets me apart from the common herd, doesn't it, Mom?

MOTHER. Perhaps, in a way.

DONNIE. And just for instance, if some woman was to come

8

along—I mean some woman I could have a real undying affection for, I guess maybe I wouldn't be too young to get married maybe, would I?

MOTHER. Donnie! You're not thinking of—

DONNIE. Certainly not. That was just merely a sort of hypothetical question, Mom. As a matter of fact, I don't think I'll ever exactly marry—

MOTHER. Oh, I see.

DONNIE. But sometimes I wonder what she sees in *me*, I honestly do.

MOTHER. Who?

DONNIE. Bertitia.

MOTHER. And who's Bertitia?

DONNIE. Aw, Mom! Well, if you must know, Bertitia is the lady who I have the honor of accompanying to the Freshman Hop tonight, that's who.

MOTHER. What's her last name, Donnie?

DONNIE. Butt. (*Sighs rapturously*) Bertitia Butt. Isn't it lovely, Mom?

MOTHER. Is she in school with you?

DONNIE. She certainly is not! She's too old for school. Gosh, she's wonderful, Mom! Just like Byron's poem, "She walks in beauty—." Only—

MOTHER. Only what?

DONNIE. Only it isn't her face. She's got a kind of beauty of spirit, if you know what I mean.

MOTHER. But, Donnie, I thought you were taking one of your friends; someone like—like Janie.

DONNIE. Janie! Mom, she's nothing but a mere infant! I guess I'd look fine showing up at an important function like the Freshman Hop with someone like Janie, now wouldn't I?

MOTHER. But you've always played with her before.

9

DONNIE. You just don't *understand*, Mom! But, gosh, I haven't got time to explain it to you, Mom! I gotta talk to Dad!

(*FADE OUT.*)

(*MUSIC: Theme music up for five seconds and under.*)

(*FADE IN.*)

(*SOUND: Footsteps running down stairs.*)

DONNIE (*slightly off mike, calls*). Say, Dad!

FATHER (*on mike*). Yes, son?

(*SOUND: Steps stop.*)

DONNIE (*on mike*). Well, I—I kind of want to ask you something, Dad.

FATHER. Ask away.

DONNIE. Well, I—

FATHER. Say, what's the idea of wearing your hat in the house?

DONNIE. Oh—why, it's merely to kind of keep my hair down.

FATHER. Take it off.

DONNIE. Aw, Dad! If I do, my hair'll be all mussed up before I even leave the house.

FATHER. Take it off, Donald.

DONNIE. Yes, sir. (*Pause*) Say, Dad, can't I bring you your slippers?

FATHER. No, thanks. Going out soon.

DONNIE. Well, then, would you like me to fill your pipe for you or something, huh, Dad?

FATHER. Your subtlety is very commendable, Donald, but just what is it you want?

DONNIE (*hesitating*). Well, look, Dad; did you ever hear of the Freshman Hop they have every year at State College?

FATHER. It seems to me I faintly remember hearing about them. Why?

DONNIE. Well, they're pretty important functions, you know. And when an outsider gets an invitation to one of them, that's considered quite an honor, 'specially if he's only a high school *junior*.

FATHER. Yes, yes, but where do I fit in?

DONNIE. Well, I guess you wouldn't want everyone talking ing about your own son, would you, Dad?

FATHER. Talking?

DONNIE. You wouldn't want them to say I had to walk to their old hop, or ride on a bus, or something, would you, Dad? 'Specially when I'm escorting a *lady?*

FATHER. Lady? Is she nice?

DONNIE. Dad, as one man to another, she's a pip!

FATHER (*amused*). So you want me to let you have the old sedan, is that it?

DONNIE. No, sir. Not exactly the sedan. Bert always takes that when he's got a date with Mildred, and he's got one tonight.

FATHER. Well?

DONNIE. Well—er—I—I kind of thought you might sort of let me have the coupé.

FATHER. You know I always use it on Lodge nights.

DONNIE. Yes, sir. But I thought just this once you might kind of like to use the bus—you know, just for a *change,* Dad.

FATHER. Well, perhaps you're right, Donald. A change might do me good.

DONNIE. Then I can have the coupé?

FATHER. Yes, I guess so, son.

DONNIE. Gosh, that's wonderful of you, Dad! I certainly appreciate it. As one man to another, you've got the soul of a—a poet!

FATHER (*laughs*). Well, that's the first time I was ever accused of that. If I'm taking the bus, (*Starts fading off mike*) I'll have to leave right now. (*Off mike*) Oh, give my regards to your "pip," will you, son?

(FADE OUT.)

(MUSIC: Theme music up for five seconds, then fade.)

(FADE IN.)

(SOUND: Doorbell rings off mike. Sound of footsteps.)

MOTHER. Yes I'm coming.

(SOUND: Footsteps. Door opens.)

MOTHER *(off mike)*. Oh, Janie!

JANIE *(off mike)*. Hello, Mrs. Hunter.

MOTHER. Come right in, Janie.

JANIE. Thanks, Mrs. Hunter.

(SOUND: Door closes. Footsteps into room as they both fade on mike.)

JANIE *(on mike)*. Is Donnie home?

MOTHER. Yes. He's getting ready to go out.

JANIE. Where's Donnie going, Mrs. Hunter?

MOTHER. To that Freshman Hop, I think.

JANIE. He *is?* How did he ever get the tickets?

MOTHER. I'm sure I don't know, Janie. *(Fading off mike, calling)* Donnie! You have a visitor!

DONNIE *(off mike)*. Thanks, Mom!

(SOUND: Footsteps running down stairs.)

MOTHER. He's coming down stairs now, Janie. Excuse me, I'll go up and see how Bert and Marjorie are coming along. *(Fades off.)*

(SOUND: Footsteps stop.)

DONNIE *(brightly)*. Hello! *(Becomes more formal when he sees JANIE)* Oh, h'lo, Janie.

JANIE *(breathless)*. Gosh!

DONNIE. What's the matter?

JANIE. Gosh, you're awful pretty!

DONNIE *(pleased)*. Like my new suit?

JANIE. It's wonderful! (*Pause*) Say, why didn't you tell me you had tickets for the hop tonight, Donnie?

DONNIE. Oh, I didn't think you'd be interested.

JANIE. Why not? I got a formal I could wear, and if—well, I mean—er—if you haven't got anyone else to take to the hop, I guess I wouldn't mind going along.

DONNIE. Thank you, but I *have* got somebody to take.

JANIE (*crestfallen*). Oh. (*Pause*) Is she—is she pretty?

DONNIE. If you don't mind, Janie, I'd prefer not to discuss her with you.

JANIE. Why not?

DONNIE. Because you wouldn't understand.

JANIE. I would, too. I guess I'm not so dumb as you think. All I asked was, is she pretty?

DONNIE. Only a poem could describe her.

> "Fair as a star when only one
> Is shining in the sky."

JANIE. Who said that?

DONNIE. Wordsworth.

JANIE. Oh! (*Pause*) Do you—do you *love* her?

DONNIE. Oh, I don't know. We sort of have a spiritual understanding.

JANIE (*gasps*). Oh! Oh! (*Starts to cry*) You—you're *mean,* that's what you are. Goodnight! (*Sobs, fades off mike.*)

DONNIE. Hey, Janie—!

(*SOUND: Footsteps retreat rapidly. Door opens and slams shut.*)

DONNIE. Aw, for gosh sakes!

(*FADE OUT.*)

(*MUSIC: Fade in theme music for a moment and then fade out.*)

A YOUNG MAN'S FANCY

(*FADE IN.*)

BERT. Well, I'm off to the races.

MOTHER. Don't be too late, Bert.

BERT. Don't you worry about me, Mom. Say, Kid—

DONNIE. Yeah, now what do you want?

BERT. Dad says you've got the keys to the coupé.

DONNIE. Certainly I have; what of it?

BERT. Let me have them. You can take the sedan.

DONNIE. I will not let you have them. Dad said—

BERT. I haven't time to argue, Sonny. Hand over those keys or—

MOTHER. Now, Bert, if your father said Donald could have the coupé—

DONNIE. I'm not going to ask Bertitia to ride in that old sedan, and that's final.

BERT. Wait a minute. Did you say "Bertitia"?

DONNIE. Certainly.

BERT. Bertitia Butt?

DONNIE. That's her name.

BERT (*laughs*). Boy, this is rich!

MOTHER. Do you know her, Bert?

BERT. Do I know her? Who doesn't? She's a standing joke around the college.

DONNIE. You shut up!

BERT. They lay bets each year on who she'll hook for the prom. She must've been pretty desperate if she had to reach down to the high school to get a date.

DONNIE. You're just jealous! She's a fine, spiritual girl and you're just too common to appreciate her.

BERT (*laughing*). It's cradle-snatching, Mom, that's what it is. I'm warning you, Kid, if you go through with it, you'll have a lot to live down in after years.

MOTHER. I think you've said enough, Bert.

14

BERT. Okay. Well, Sonny, if you want to play the dog in the manger and keep the coupé—

DONNIE. I most certainly do.

BERT. I guess I can manage. Goodnight, Kid. So long, Mom. (*Fades off.*)

(*SOUND: Footsteps retreating. Door opens and closes.*)

DONNIE. Why, the—the—!

MOTHER. I'm sure Bert was exaggerating, Donnie.

DONNIE. Huh! You don't think I'd let anything *he* said bother me?

MOTHER. That's right. You just don't pay any attention to it. I'm sure you'll have a very nice time—

(*SOUND: Telephone rings.*)

MOTHER. Now, I wonder who that is—?

(*SOUND: Footsteps. Ring. Receiver lifted from hook.*)

MOTHER. Hello?—Yes, yes, he is. Hold on a minute, please. It's for you, Donnie.

DONNIE. Me? Gee, I wonder who— Thanks, Mom. Hello— Uh-huh— Oh, hello, Miss Butt— What?— Oh— Oh, no, I don't mind— Uh-huh. Sure, some other time. G'bye.

(*SOUND: Receiver replaced on hook.*)

MOTHER. Why, what is it, dear?

DONNIE (*very tragic*). She can't go. She's got a headache.

MOTHER. Oh, I'm sorry, Donnie.

DONNIE (*trying not to cry*). Oh, Mom! Mom!

MOTHER. There, there! Now it really isn't as bad as all that.

DONNIE.   "The weariness, the fever, and the fret,
           Here where men sit and hear each other groan—"

MOTHER. Byron?

DONNIE. Keats.

MOTHER. Yes, I should have known.

DONNIE. Well, I guess I'll go to bed.

15

MOTHER. It seems a shame to waste the tickets.

DONNIE (*begins to brighten*). It does at that.

MOTHER. Why don't you—?

DONNIE (*excited*). No, don't tell me, I know!

(*SOUND: Receiver lifted off telephone hurriedly.*)

DONNIE (*excited*). Hello— Hello— Give me eight-one-three-five— Yes— Gee! Why can't they hurry? Why do they—? Hello!—Hello, Janie?—Listen, you get that formal of yours out of the mothballs!—Why? Because you and me are going places, that's why!

(*MUSIC: Theme music comes up for ten seconds to announcer's sign off.*)

GRAMPS

By

MERRILL ROGERS

CAST

GRAMPS
BOBBY
GENERAL GRANT
GENERAL LEE

GRAMPS

ANNOUNCER. Most of you who were born sometime, we'll say, before the second decade of the present century, have a vivid recollection of at least one old veteran of the Civil War—or, as they call it below the Mason and Dixon Line, the War Between the States. Perhaps he was your own grandfather and, like Bobby's grandfather, told you tales of his martial exploits that made up in glamor and romantic quality for what, at times, they may have lacked in downright truthfulness. Though quite likely, the old gentleman told those stories so often he came to believe them himself. I hope he did. Just as I hope Bobby's Gramps believed the stories he told Bobby. And especially about the time when— But let's hear it as it must have sounded to Bobby some thirty or more years ago.

GRAMPS (*fading in*). Gittin' pretty near your bed time, Bobby. Your Ma ain't goin' to like it unless you start gittin' undressed and ready pretty soon.

(GRAMPS' *voice is that of an old man of seventy-odd and has the slight drawl of a Down-East Yankee.*)

BOBBY. But just *one* story, Gramps. About the war. And then I'll go right to bed.

GRAMPS. Well, mebbe there's time for just one story.

BOBBY (*eagerly*). Tell me about the Battle of Gettysburg. And how you and Cap Slocum stopped Pickett's Charge.

GRAMPS. I've told you that one so of'n I sh'd think you'd know it back'ards and for'ards by now. . . . But mebbe I'll tell

you one I ain't never told anyone before. One that's a hull lot
more important than any battle.

BOBBY. More important than *any battle,* Gramps?

GRAMPS. That's right, Bobby. An' it's somethin' I'm prouder
about than anything that ever happened to me.

BOBBY. Gee, Gramps!

GRAMPS. Now you just wait till I git my pipe goin' . . .

(*SOUND: Match struck. Drawing on pipe.*)

You see, we wuz in camp down there in Virginia. And the
war had been goin' on for pretty nigh to four years and we
wuz still a-fightin'. And after four years, Bobby, you git to
look at things diff'rent than you did when you first marched
out in a brand new uniform.

BOBBY. And the band playing.

GRAMPS. That's it, Bobby. . . . Well, I remember 'twas along
towards the middle o' the afternoon. I'd been washin' out
my socks and while I wuz waitin' for 'em to dry, I wuz
settin' there on a log thinkin' about things. An' while I was
settin' there up came the Sergeant and sez Gen'ral Grant wuz
mighty anxious to see me.

BOBBY. General Grant?

GRAMP. Gen'ral Grant. So natcher'ly I sez, "Tell the Gen'ral
I'll be right along," and started to put on my socks.

BOBBY. Didn't you wait for your socks to get dry, Gramps?

GRAMPS. Shucks no, Bobby. I just put 'em on wet. When you're
in a war a little thing like wet socks don't bother you none.

BOBBY. But wouldn't you catch cold?

GRAMPS. Oh, no. . . . Well, anyway, I started for Gen'ral
Grant's tent. He was mighty busy workin' at a table with a
lot of papers on it but when I got there he looked up and he
sez—

20

GRAMPS

GEN'L GRANT (*fading in*). Hello, Gramps. Come in and sit down. I wanted to talk to you. . . . I've been sort of worried.

(GENERAL GRANT *has a slight twang.* GRAMPS' *voice remains the same.*)

GRAMPS. That's too bad, Gen'ral. What're you worryin' about?

GEN'L GRANT. It's about this war, Gramps.

GRAMPS. Well, I've been sort of worryin' about it myself, Gen'ral. Wonderin' if it wuz ever goin' to end?

GEN'L GRANT. We've been doing pretty well so far, Gramps. But not well enough.

GRAMPS. Looks like them Johnny Rebs 've still got a lot of fight left in 'em, Gen'ral.

GEN'L GRANT. That's the truth, Gramps. And what I wanted to know is whether you've got any ideas that will get 'em licked any quicker.

GRAMPS. Well, now, that's a sort of a tough question, ain't it, Gen'ral Grant?

GEN'L GRANT. I know it is, Gramps. When I first came here to Virginia I said I was going to fight it out on this line if it took all summer.

GRAMPS. I remember you said that, Gen'ral.

GEN'L GRANT. But it's been all winter too. And here it is Spring. And a lot of people are getting sick of the whole business.

GRAMPS. You're not tellin' me any news, Gen'ral. I've got a girl up North named Gramma. And she's pretty sick of this war.

GEN'L GRANT. I can appreciate how she feels.

GRAMPS. And my Aunt Sarah keeps writin' me all the time an' askin' me when I'm goin' to come home an' git to work on the farm. An' you know how it is explainin' to women folks, Gen'ral. They think you're just tryin' to git out of doin' the chores.

GEN'L GRANT. Your Aunt Sarah is right though, Gramps. All you boys ought to be back on the farm. But we've got to finish up this war first.

GRAMPS (*a little doggedly*). If you ask me, Gen'ral, we'd of all been a sight better off if this war'd never got started.

GEN'L GRANT. Well, that's one way of looking at it, Gramps. But I'm a little surprised at your talking that way.

GRAMPS. I've been thinkin' about it a hull lot lately. . . . What's been the good of all this shootin' an' killin', Gen'ral? What's been the good of it?

GEN'L GRANT. I'm just as anxious to get it over as you are, Gramps. But the question is *how* are we going to do it?

GRAMPS. Well, I tell you, Gen'ral. I've had an idea in my head now for quite a spell. Why don't you go an' have a talk with Gen'ral Lee?

GEN'L GRANT. Talk with General Lee?

GRAMPS. Just sit down—the two of you. An' talk the whole thing over. Mebbe you could find some way to stop all this shootin' and killin'.

GEN'L GRANT. Why, *I* couldn't do that, Gramps. I'm a soldier. My business is fighting—not talking.

GRAMPS. That doesn't mean you have to keep on fightin' the whole gol-durned time, does it, Gen'ral?

GEN'L GRANT. That's my job, Gramps. That's what the President hired me for.

GRAMPS. You might find Gen'ral Lee's a dang sight more reasonable than you think he is, Gen'ral.

GEN'L GRANT. Maybe he is, Gramps. But that's not up to me. If there's any talking to be done, Gen'ral Lee's got to make the first move.

GRAMPS. Now, Gen'ral, you're just bein' stubborn.

GEN'L GRANT. Well, maybe I am, Gramps. But the first move on anything of that sort has got to come from General Lee. And that's flat.

GRAMPS. What difference does it make *who* makes the first move? The best thing anyone can do about this war—or any war—besides not *startin'* it in the first place—is to *stop* it. An' most people ain't goin' to care *how* you stop it, so long as you *do* stop it.

GEN'L GRANT. Well, you've been a mighty good soldier, Gramps, And I'm not going to say anything about *that* point of view. But I'm a little disappointed in you just the same. I thought you might give me a real idea.

GRAMPS. Well, I thought I wuz givin' you a real idea.

GEN'L GRANT. Not that sort of an idea. That isn't going to help anything right now.

GRAMPS (*a little huffily*). Well, I'm sorry you're disapp'inted in me, Gen'ral. But of course, if that's the way you look at it—

GEN'L GRANT. Now, don't feel that way, Gramps. I appreciate your trying to give me a hand, but I guess I'll just have to figure it myself the best way I can.

GRAMPS. All right then, Gen'ral. The Sergeant said somethin' about mebbe we'd be havin' another battle tomorrow. In which case I'll go back an' finish dryin' out my socks.

(*Pause.*)

BOBBY (*fading in*). Did General Grant think you were mad at him?

GRAMPS. No, I guess he knew I wasn't mad at him. But we just didn't see eye to eye on this business, that's all. An' of course, bein' the Gen'ral, he natcher'ly had the last word.

BOBBY. What did you do, Gramps? Go back and finish drying out your socks?

GRAMPS. That's what I did. But the more I got to thinkin' about what I'd said to Gen'ral Grant, the more common-sensical it all seemed. And all of a sudden I got another idee which seemed to bust all over me.

BOBBY. Another idea, Gramps?

GRAMPS. Yes, sir. I sez to myself: "If Gen'ral Grant won't do nothin' about it, why I'll go see Gen'ral Lee."

BOBBY. General Lee?

GRAMPS. That's what I sez to myself. So that very night I snuck out of camp and started fast as I could leg it down the road to the camp where the Johnny Rebs were. An' when I got there I hitched up my pants an' went up to their sentry feller an' told him I'd come to see the head Gen'ral.

BOBBY. What did the sentry say?

GRAMPS. Well, he hemmed an' he hawed an' sez it wuzn't the way they usually did things but fin'lly he 'lowed he'd see what he could do. An' sure enough pretty soon he came back an' took me to where Gen'ral Lee wuz.

BOBBY. And what did General Lee look like, Gramps?

GRAMPS. He wuz tall an' very stately an' dignified lookin'. Anyone could of told he wuz a soldier—every inch of him. Only he wuz sort of gentle lookin' too. An' sad. An' you could see he wuz sort of worried about things—just the same as Gen'ral Grant. But when he saw me he just sort of smiled an'—

GEN'L LEE (*fading in*). They tell me you wanted to see me, Gramps.

(GENERAL LEE's *voice is that of a cultured gentleman but without any suggestion of a "Southern accent."*)

GRAMPS. That's what I come for, Gen'ral Lee. It's mighty kind of you to take the time when I know you must be so busy and everything.

GEN'L LEE. That's quite all right, Gramps. I *am* busy, but I understand it's something pretty important.

GRAMPS. Well, *I* think it's pretty important, Gen'ral. Elsewise I wouldn't of taken the chance to come all the way down here in my blue uniform an' risk gettin' shot at.

GEN'L LEE. I'm glad nobody shot you, Gramps.

GRAMPS. I'll tell you what I come to see you about, Gen'ral. You see, I wuz talkin' to Gen'ral Grant just this afternoon. About how we could put an end to this war.

GEN'L LEE. An end to the war?

GRAMPS. I got the idee mebbe we c'd do it without havin' to fight no more battles. You an' him could git together somehow an' sit down an' settle it.

GEN'L LEE (slowly). It's not as simple as that, Gramps. The only way for a soldier to settle anything is by fighting.

GRAMPS. That's just what Gen'ral Grant sez. I didn't git no satisfaction from him at all.

GEN'L LEE. General Grant is a mighty fine soldier. I can see how he'd look at it that way.

GRAMPS. He's a mighty fine soldier all right, Gen'ral. But sometimes he's as stubborn as a mule.

GEN'L LEE. You have to be stubborn sometimes, Gramps.

GRAMPS. Well, anyway, what I had in mind wuz, if *you* could sort o' make the fust move—

GEN'L LEE. Me, Gramps?

GRAMPS. Just let Gen'ral Grant know you wuz willin' to talk.

GEN'L LEE (slowly). I'll have to admit things don't look so good for us right now, Gramps. We've been losing quite a few battles lately.

GRAMPS. I wuzn't thinkin' of that so much, Gen'ral.

GEN'L LEE. And our uniforms have had so much wear and tear they're starting to give out. And some of the boys have holes right through the soles of their shoes. But that doesn't mean we're licked, Gramps. Not by a long shot.

GRAMPS. I wuzn't sayin' you wuz licked, Gen'ral.

GEN'L LEE. Our boys haven't lost any of their grit. And the next battle we fight we'll show you good and proper.

GRAMPS. Well, mebbe that's true, Gen'ral. But my point is what's the use of keepin' this war goin'?

GEN'L LEE. Oh, Gramps! When anyone asks me a question like that it makes me feel sad.

GRAMPS. It makes everybody feel sad, Gen'ral. So long as nobody seems to git the answer to it.

GEN'L LEE. I know. We've been at it for four pretty terrible years, haven't we?

GRAMPS. That's right. An' the fightin's still goin' on.

GEN'L LEE (*proudly*). Yes, Gramps. The South is still fighting.

GRAMPS. Why does it *have* to go on, Gen'ral?

GEN'L LEE (*sadly*). Because it has to, Gramps.

GRAMPS. With thousands o' *more* boys to be killed—like pigs in a slaughter house.

GEN'L LEE. I'm afraid so, Gramps.

GRAMPS (*passionately*). The war ought never been allowed to git started in the fust place, Gen'ral Lee. Back there at the time we wuz arguin' about the Union—somebody oughter of done somethin' about it *then*.

GEN'L LEE. Perhaps you're right, Gramps. But so long as a man remains—to defend the South—

GRAMPS. If you an' Gen'ral Grant sat down an' talked it all out, you could stop it tomorrow.

GEN'L LEE. Not now, Gramps. . . . Besides, even if I were willing, you say General Grant isn't.

GRAMPS. He won't make the fust move, that's all, Gen'ral.

GEN'L LEE. If I make the first move, Gramps, people would think it was because—well—

GRAMPS (*a little angrily*). Fiddlesticks, Gen'ral. Everybody knows what tough fighters you Johnny Rebs have been.

They'll just give you credit for havin' a heap more sense than anybody in the whole shebang. An' a lot more gumption.

GEN'L LEE. Perhaps so, Gramps.

GRAMPS. Mind you, I can't promise anything what Gen'ral Grant would say. He might want to argue pretty strong about you fellers comin' back to the Union.

GEN'L LEE. I—imagine he would, Gramps.

GRAMPS. An' after all, Gen'ral, we had a pretty good nation before we got to fightin' among ourselves. An' once we got the fightin' out of our system mebbe we could all see that one big country wuz a lot better than two little ones.

GEN'L LEE. I've thought about that, Gramps.

GRAMPS. You come from Virginia, Gen'ral. An' Gen'ral Grant comes from Missouri. An' I come from the State o' Maine. But when you add it all up, Gen'ral, we're all Americans.

GEN'L LEE. Even if I did offer to talk to General Grant, Gramps, I couldn't make any promises as to what I'd say.

GRAMPS. I ain't askin' you to make any promises, Gen'ral— neither of you. I'm only askin' you an' Gen'ral Grant to sit down together. Because if you'd only try it, Gen'ral, the both of you might git to see that whatever it wuz got us all fightin' each other, it ain't worth the life of another boy—whether he's got on a blue uniform or a gray. (*Pause. Then beseechingly.*) Will you do it, Gen'ral?

GEN'L LEE. I was just looking out over those mountains, Gramps. Whenever I want to think about anything I like to look at them.

GRAMPS. I know. It's like that psalmist feller—who wrote about liftin' up your eyes to the hills.

GEN'L LEE. King David it was, Gramps.

GRAMPS. King David. (*Pause. Then softly*) Will you do it, Gen'ral Lee?

27

GRAMPS

GEN'L LEE (*quietly*). I'll do it, Gramps.

GRAMPS (*heartily*). That's fine, Gen'ral. I'll go back an' tell Gen'ral Grant an' fix it up for him to meet you. Say, day after tomorrow.

GEN'L LEE. The sooner the better, Gramps—if we're going to make a try. . . . Whereabouts shall we meet?

GRAMPS. I know a place, Gen'ral. I noticed it while I was comin' down here. It's sort of quiet an' it'd be convenient for both parties. . . . It's a little town they call Appomatox Court House.

(*Pause.*)

BOBBY (*fading in*). Is that all, Gramps?

GRAMPS. That's all, Bobby. Now, it's time for you to git to bed before your Ma comes up an' finds you.

BOBBY. But you didn't tell me what they said—when General Lee and General Grant got together.

GRAMPS. I never did know what they said, Bobby. Because when they got to the place they just went into a back room an' shut the door. An' they stayed there a long time—just talkin'—the way I'd hoped they would. But when they come out, I c'd see Gen'ral Lee didn't look worried any more. An' neither did Gen'ral Grant. They were both just sort of quiet and sober lookin'. An' then they shook hands an' Gen'ral Lee got on his horse an' rode away an' Gen'ral Grant an' I rode back to our own camp. An' the Gen'ral never opened his mouth all the way until he got off his horse. An' then he looked at me sort of queer-like an' said. "America is proud of you, Gramps." An' he stood very stiff for a second an' then jerked his hand up to the vizor of his hat an' saluted me. An' then he went into his tent. An' the next day we learned the war wuz over an' we c'd all go home.

BOBBY. And there wasn't any more shooting and killing?

28

GRAMPS

GRAMPS. There wa'n't any more shootin' and killin'. An' that's
the reason I said, Bobby, I wuz prouder o' that than anythin'
that ever happened to me. An' if you forget all the stories
of the battles I've told you about an' just remember this one,
you'll have somethin' that'll be mighty important to you
when you grow up to be a man. . . . An' now you git to bed,
Bobby, just as fast as you can git them buttons unbuttoned.

ONE EGG

By

BABETTE HUGHES

CAST

A Young Man
A Girl
A Waiter

ONE EGG

(*MUSIC: Up and fade behind.*)

ANNOUNCER. The ——— Players present "One Egg," a farce in one act by Babette Hughes. The scene is a small restaurant in New York City about eleven o'clock in the morning. There are no customers in the restaurant and the one waiter is passing the time putting away silverware and rearranging the dishes. In a few seconds, he is interrupted by the entrance of a Young Man with a manuscript under one arm, a package of new paper under the other, and a number of neatly sharpened pencils in one hand.

(*MUSIC: Up and out to.*)

(*SOUND: Clatter of dishes and silverware.*)

(*SOUND: Door opens slightly remote—clatter stops.*)

MAN (*off mike*). Hello, King Tut.

(*SOUND: Door closes.*)

MAN (*fades in*). Well, well, well—no one here. How's the hash today?

WAITER. Fine, sir, and how are you?

MAN. Me? Say, I've even got it all over the hash. I'm feeling great . . . better than a Scotchman who has found a thousand dollars.

WAITER. And have you found a thousand dollars, sir?

MAN. Well, not exactly. But if I get a couple of good ideas and work three or four hours I may get enough for my rent and a sirloin steak. Sounds promising, doesn't it?

ONE EGG

WAITER. Yes, sir, very. Will you sit here?

MAN. Sure, anywhere.

(*SOUND: Paper falling.*)

WAITER. You dropped your package.

MAN. Thanks. Put it on the table. I'll want it.

WAITER. Yes, sir, and how will you have the steak . . . rare, medium, or well done?

MAN. You old killjoy! That was a promise, not an order. I'll eat later but I want to work now, so get out and leave me alone for a while.

WAITER. Yes, sir.

MAN. Do you see this paper and these pencils? Well, they're going to get together with a bang, understand?

(*SOUND: Bangs hand on table.*)

WAITER. Yes, sir, but what was it you wanted me to do?

MAN. Disappear, dumb-bell! Go drown yourself in the dressing or vanish in vinegar or vanilla . . . but go out in the kitchen to do it.

WAITER. Yes, sir.

MAN. Wait a minute! What's your hurry? I want some literary advice. I'll explain the situation. I have a friend and he said to me. . . . You can sit down. (*Pause*) I said you could sit down!

WAITER. Yes, sir!

MAN. Well, why don't you?

WAITER. Oh, were you talking to me, sir? I thought that was in the story.

MAN. No; that wasn't in the story. (*Pause*) Well, are you going to sit down?

WAITER. No, sir. I'm not tired.

MAN. Skip it. Well, he said to me: "Do you want to make some money?"

34

WAITER. Yes, sir . . . I'd like to very much.

MAN. Oh, you would? Well, I'm sorry, but I can't help you. So he said, "How would you like to make some money?"

WAITER. I said I'd like it fine, sir.

MAN. Say . . . will you let me finish my story? That's what the man said to me; not what I'm saying to you! Do you get me?

WAITER. No, sir. Who were you saying it to?

MAN. You, you old green cheese. But the man said it to me. Now do you understand?

WAITER. No, sir.

MAN. All right. I'll go on with it, but don't interrupt again if you ever want to carry another tray. This friend of mine is an actor and he's got a pull with the management of some vaudeville circuit. Someone dropped out of their bill and they told my friend to bring around an act for a fellow and a girl and they'd give him a chance to fill in.

WAITER. That was nice of them.

MAN. Well, my friend called me and said he'd pay me fifty bucks for a good snappy twenty minute act by this evening. Being a little fed up with writing purely for pleasure and artistic value, I couldn't exactly say "no" to a handful of cold cash.

WAITER. Of course not, sir.

MAN. That's the story in a nutshell. Now tell me, does anything funny ever happen here? Any amusing situations. You know, the sort of thing that happens every second and no one can ever think of. Tell me all about it now.

WAITER. What do you want me to tell you, sir?

MAN. Well, let's see how I can throw some light on it.

(SOUND: Click of light switch.)

MAN. No; not that kind of light. You've seen comedies, haven't

35

you? Well, I thought a restaurant scene with a few complications might be good. That's why I'm appealing to you.

WAITER. I see.

MAN. A restaurant is the root of comedy. It has all the elements . . . noodles three feet long . . . soup with hair in it . . . prehistoric hash . . . onions . . . corn beef in French, Russian, Spanish and Chinese . . . a million and one possibilities if I could only think how to use them. Now tell me, does anything funny ever happen here?

WAITER. Funny? Oh, no sir . . . nothing funny. We have accidents, sir, but *very* seldom.

MAN. Well, go and have one now . . . the kind that prevents you from ever having another.

WAITER. Yes, sir.

MAN. This is an awful mess!

(*SOUND: Doors opens and shuts.*)

MAN. How about a nice little nip of . . . Oh, I beg your pardon. Where did you come from?

GIRL (*remote*). I beg *your* pardon.

(GIRL's *speeches remote until* MAN *moves to her table.*)

MAN. I thought King Tut was still here.

GIRL. You might have looked before you started screeching.

MAN. I don't screech.

GIRL. That's a matter of opinion.

MAN. I don't suppose you carry lemonade on your hip or in your handbag, do you? That's all right, don't look. I'll wait until King Tut comes around with the breakfast programs. I shouldn't drink now anyway. It might extinguish my creative light.

GIRL. Are you hired by this restaurant to drive away customers?

MAN. Don't go. You'd better take off your things and stay. It's raining out.

GIRL. What difference does it make to you if I should get wet?

MAN. I have such a sympathetic nature that it has a very bad effect on my mind to see *anyone* get wet. It really disturbs me almost as much as getting wet myself.

GIRL. Of all the impertinence . . .

MAN. All right, go ahead. But you won't find a better restaurant. Their cooking is wonderful . . . at least their eggs are. . . . I've never had anything else. It's very inexpensive, too. There! That's fine. You sit right there and King Tut will be along in a minute. Unless he's gone to sleep for another thousand years. (*Calling*) Hey there, King Tut . . . come out of your tomb! We want breakfast!

WAITER (*remote*). Did you call me, sir?

MAN. No; I called the ghost of your great dead ancestor to see if we'd get any breakfast this morning . . . but you'll do.

WAITER (*fading in*). Oh, good morning Miss. Will you have breakfast?

GIRL. Yes, please. I want coffee, and . . . let me see. . . . Are your eggs newly laid?

WAITER. Oh, yes ma'am . . . as fresh as a flower.

GIRL. I'll have one boiled egg. Coffee and one egg.

WAITER. We can't serve one egg, ma'am . . . you'll have to order two.

GIRL. I won't have two. This is ridiculous. Why won't you serve me one egg if I want one?

WAITER. I don't know, ma'am. We just never do.

GIRL. I never heard anything like this in all my life. I always take one egg . . . every morning of my life I've eaten one egg, and in better places than this, too. You must be mistaken.

WAITER. No, ma'am, I'm not. The management won't allow one.

37

GIRL. Go and ask the cook if he won't cook one egg especially . . . for me.

WAITER. Especially how, ma'am?

GIRL. Just especially.

WAITER. Yes, ma'am. (*Fading out*) One egg . . . especially.

MAN. It must become rather monotonous. (*Pause*) I said it must get on your nerves rather.

GIRL (*superciliously and meaningly*). It does!

MAN. Yes; two or three times a week does me.

GIRL. What *are* you talking about?

MAN. Eggs, of course . . . weren't you?

GIRL. I wasn't talking with you about anything.

MAN. Don't look now, but here comes your egg *especially*.

GIRL. Well . . .

WAITER (*fading in*). The cook said, ma'am, that he won't do anything particularly.

GIRL. The cook won't do anything?

WAITER. Not the way you said, he won't.

GIRL. Well, what shall I do? I'm dreadfully hungry. I haven't had a thing to eat since last night.

WAITER. You might take two eggs.

GIRL. I won't. I refuse to order what I don't want. I never take two eggs. Do you understand?

MAN (*hopefully*). I always eat one egg for breakfast.

GIRL. Well . . .

MAN. If we could get together . . . you order one and I'll order one and we'll have . . .

WAITER (*excited*). Two!!!

MAN. No!!! One . . . order.

GIRL. I don't know whether I want to or not.

MAN. Well, of course, that's up to you . . . but if you really want your egg I'd suggest . . .

38

ONE EGG

GIRL. I do! Yes, I will!

MAN. What? Love, honor and obey?

GIRL. I'll have my egg soft-boiled.

MAN. Terrible . . . soft-boiled . . . how feminine. I'll have *my egg* fried.

WAITER. Yes, sir. (*Fading out*) One soft-boiled egg and one fried egg.

MAN. Now, to make it easier for the waiter, I'll move over to your table.

GIRL. I don't think it's necessary.

MAN. Think of all the energy saved . . . and we'll feel quite at home.

GIRL. I suppose I might as well go through with it.

MAN. If I had nothing to worry about this would be perfect! You see, I'm trying to think of something funny . . . to write a vaudeville sketch about . . . a little comedy scene. If you could help me . . .

GIRL. I help you! I'm not interested in you at all . . . don't even care to know who you are.

MAN. That's right, you don't. My name is Christopher Preserve. Not . . .

GIRL. Chris Preserve! Don't you remember me . . . at Dartmoor University?

MAN. I went there . . . but . . .

GIRL. Mary Cross . . . now, don't you remember?

MAN. Of course I do . . . at Dartmoor! Why it's been so long since I've seen you . . . four years . . . ever since graduation.

GIRL. Heavens, but I'm glad to see you! How is your writing coming . . . does it really pay for your bread and butter?

MAN. For all I get . . . which isn't much. Which is the reason I always eat *one* egg. . . . Speaking of eggs . . . he's in again.

WAITER (*fading in*). I'm sorry, sir, but you can't have two different kinds of eggs. You can have two fried eggs, or two boiled eggs, but not one fried egg and one boiled egg. We don't mix them, sir.

MAN. We don't want them mixed . . . we want them separate.

GIRL. Do be sensible, Chris. Don't you ever part an order?

WAITER. The cook says that two eggs belong together.

MAN. It must be his family tradition. How romantic. What God has put together let no man put asunder. Ask your cook if a chicken lays two eggs at once.

WAITER. I don't think they do, sir . . .

GIRL. Never mind, Waiter . . . we'll have two soft-boiled eggs.

MAN. Oh, no, Mary! I'm very fond of you, but I can't bear soft eggs . . . hard, however . . . I can put up with.

GIRL. Very well. We'll have one hard- and one soft-boiled egg.

WAITER. Yes, ma'am. (*Fading out*) I'll try.

GIRL. There! That's settled . . . by means of a woman's tact. I do hope he hurries. . . . I'm almost desperate.

MAN. While we're waiting, you can tell me how you happened to come down to this out-of-the-way place. You used to live 'way up town.

GIRL. I still do . . . but I had to escape this morning.

MAN. Are you being pursued?

GIRL. No. Dad is conducting a contest and if I had stayed, I would have been drafted as a judge.

MAN. Perhaps I should know, but what sort of a contest . . . beauty, cooking, recipes, or rhymes that go: "There was a young man named Potato who sat on a juicy tomato," etc.

GIRL. Nothing like that, but fully as bad. You see, Dad is in the vaudeville business.

MAN. I should have known.

GIRL. He's looking for a new man to do scripts for him. It's my job to read through a stack of manuscripts until I find one at all good. This time I got out though . . . you can imagine the sort of stuff that comes in.

MAN. Yes, I guess I can.

GIRL. It bores me to death. It wouldn't get a smile out of a laughing hyena. . . . Hurrah! The eggs at last.

MAN. I don't see any eggs.

WAITER (*fading in*). The boiled eggs, sir . . .

GIRL. What did the cook say this time?

WAITER. He said it was a very singular order. He said a lot more, too, sir, but it wasn't about eggs, sir. . . .

GIRL. This situation is becoming impossible! I'm starved.

MAN. Waiter, bring us each a hot cup of coffee. Hurry, and by the time it's ready, I'll have thought.

WAITER. Yes, sir. (*Fading out*) I hope so, sir.

GIRL. What impertinence! He seems dreadfully impatient.

MAN. Maybe he's hungry too. And the cook won't give him anything to eat.

GIRL. You know, I'm sure you're just the man Father needs. While we're waiting, let's write the scenario for an act and then you could show it to him. I was thinking, this egg situation bringing us together . . .

MAN. What a lovely thought. It *has* brought us together, hasn't it? Maybe forever!

GIRL. I mean bringing us together at the same table. It would make a delightful idea for a comedy and I've even thought of a wonderful title . . . "One Egg."

MAN. Play, nothing! That's a myth!

GIRL. The scene will be in a restaurant like this one. The man will be sitting at a table . . .

MAN. He'd be writing.

GIRL. Of course! Then the girl will enter and order one egg . . . and the waiter will refuse to bring it . . . and the man will say . . .

MAN. "I always eat one egg for breakfast." The two get together and order two eggs. The eggs must be symbolic. How beautiful . . . their destinies are forever joined . . .

GIRL. In a frying-pan.

MAN. Yes; books on playwriting always say that plays like this should build up to the curtain line and that should be the big punch. Here everything depends on whether they get the eggs and how they are to be cooked.

GIRL. That's it . . . what way *shall* they be cooked, then? There are boiled eggs, poached eggs, coddled eggs and . . .

MAN AND GIRL (*together*). *Scrambled eggs!*

MAN. They will unscramble the plot!

GIRL. I adore scrambled eggs!

MAN. That's the curtain line. The hero will turn to the waiter, and say, "Scrambled eggs, please!"

WAITER (*remote*). Yes sir. Scrambled eggs!

GIRL. Oh, he was right there. . . .

MAN. Right there for the punch line.

(*MUSIC: Up.*)

TWO RADIO MONOLOGUES

By

SYLVIA CLARK

ROSIE AT THE TRAIN

A Monologue

By

SYLVIA CLARK

ANNOUNCER. The setting is the Grand Central Station, the time, a few minutes before one o'clock. Big Sister Rosie is shepherding a small army of relatives toward the crowded waiting room to see sister Essie off on the train—and here they come— (*SOUND: Taxi horns and noises of Grand Central Station.*)

ROSIE (*fades in: excited*). Come on, Mama, hurry up, Essie, you'll never make it. It's one o'clock already and the train leaves exactly at three. Come on, Mama, stick to me, you'll get lost. Albert, you get the porter, and I'll pay the taxi. No, no, I'll get the porter and you pay the taxi. Come on, everybody. Porter, porter, will you take these grips. Take that one, and that one, and that one. No, I'll take that one. Yes, she'll take that one. No, I'll take that one. Well, you take them all. I'll give you five cents in stamps later. Essie, have you got your magazine? Where's your candy? No, I haven't got the candy. Ella, have you got the candy? Lena, have you got the candy? Mom, have you got the candy? Say, listen, who has the peanut brittle? Oh, look! The porter has the candy! (*Laughs*) Come on, everybody, we haven't much time. Stick to me and you'll wear time-tables. I wonder where we go—I'll ask this fella. Pardon me, Mister, is this the way to the Syracuse? One

45

o'clock standard Eastern? Two o'clock? Why, where is the one o'clock? Oh, the one o'clock leaves at two o'clock? Oh, the two o'clock leaves at one o'clock? The one o'clock leaves at three o'clock? What do you have to do? Get an adding machine to catch a train nowadays? What I'd like to know, Mister, does the train leave at one, two, or three o'clock? Make up your mind. (*Aside*) He says the train leaves right behind the engine. They make you sick. You get nervous prosperity before you leave town—

(*SOUND: Whistle. Toot toot.*)

VOICE (*offstage*). All aboard! On track number blaa-blaa and blaa-blaa and blaa-blaa and blaa—and all points West!

ROSIE. That helped a lot! Where is this town—Blaa-blaa and blaa-blaa? They put a goop out there to make it tough for you. It's a good thing you're only going to Syracuse. When you go to California, you have to take an interpreter along. Wait a minute, I'll ask this guy—he has a high forehead. Excuse me, Mister, when the man says, "Blaa-blaa and Blaa-blaa," does he mean Syracuse? I say, when he says, "Blaa-blaa and Blaa-blaa," does he mean Syracuse? Oh yeah? 18 million English-speaking people in this depot and I gotta pick on a Greek!

VOICE (*offstage*). All ab-yoooord! Trains for Syracuse on track number neahnnyy-neahnnyy!

ROSIE. Listen to that! I guess he broke his blaa-blaa— Now he bleats like a nanny-goat. Well, come on, everybody. He must mean something. A man wouldn't stand around and "neahnnyy" without a reason. Porter, porter, where's the porter? Where's the porter? Did he get lost? *That's* got to happen now. Lady, did you see a colored porter with a red cap on his head? Oh, there he is! No, that's not him. No, there he is. No, that's not him. Oh, my goodness—there's a million of them! Albert, look for the one with the gold tooth in the front. Come on, Mama, hurry up, Essie. Hurry up, here's your train. Car 34—

(SOUND: Toot toot whistle and bell.)

Hurry up, get on!

(SOUND: Train puffing.)

Where's your ticket? You did not give me your ticket! Mama, did she give me the ticket? Mama, I ask you like a daughter, looking you right in the face, *did she give me the ticket?*

(SOUND: Whistle.)

Oh, my goodness, where's the ticket? Oh, for Heaven's sake, hold the train! With both hands, Albert! Oh, I wouldn't have a nail left! Where's the ticket? Who? Where? In my hand? Now, who put that ticket in my hand? I am not *excited. I am cool and corrected.* Here, Mister. Yeah, my sister is the only one that's going. Come on, Ella, come on, Jennie, come on, Mama. What! Yeah, mister, they're all with me. Well, I guess they can go in if they want to. Oh, is that so? Don't argue with him, Mama. He's only the ticket taker. Go ahead, Essie. I'll write to the president of the railroad about him. Who can't write? I can write when I want to. Fresh thing, did you hear what he said? Wants to know where the convention's going. Well, it's nobody's business. Go right along, it's car 34!

(SOUND: Toot toot.)

Come on, everybody, hurry up. Hurry up, Essie, get on. Never mind, you can kiss Mama when you come home. Hurry up, you only got an hour and a half. Have a good time. Goodbye. Go down to the winder. Come on, everybody, come down to the winder. Come on, Mama, come down to the winder. Come on, Ella, come down to the winder. Pull up your stocking, Mama. Come down to the winder. There she is! She's

47

by the winder. Isn't she sun-burned already? No, that's the porter. There she is by the other winder. Hello, Yoo-hoo, you're by the winder. You're by the winder, stay there. (*Aside*) She's by the winder. Our own flesh and blood is by the winder. Look! Mama, she knows you, mama. Right through the winder. She looks better already. The trip is doing you good, so is the railroad. Open the winder! Open the winder. Don't be afraid, you paid for your ticket. You can't open the winder? She can't open the winder. Poor kid, she's weak. Never mind, you'll be strong when you get back. Don't forget to take your pills. Pills! She can't hear me. Pills! Watch my fingers. P-i-l-l-s! That's right. Not the ones in the pink box, the ones in the blue box. The blue. The blue. The BA-LOOOO! My goodness, you have to explode to tell her anything. It's terrible. There should be a hole in the winder. Have a good time and if anyone dies, we'll let you know. Write to Aunt Bertha. Aunt Bertha. That's right. Tell her you hope her gallstones get better. Better. Not bigger. Better. That's right. Don't push your nose against the winder. You look funny. You look like Uncle Albert. Uncle Albert. The nose was born and the body grew on afterwards. Ha, ha, ha! Oh, I got a stitch. Take good care of yourself. Drop us a line when you get there, so we'll know you weren't killed or anything. Killed. Killed! Look! (*Strangles*) Oh, I nearly choked myself! Yoo-hoo! Have you got your lunch? Well, eat your bananas before they get black. Ha, ha, ha! She's crazy. Don't get kidnaped by any man (*Aside*) What? Mama says, no such luck.

(*SOUND: Whistle and bells.*)

Goodbye. Goodbye! What's the matter with the train? Why doesn't it move? Something must be the matter. Come to the platform. Come to the platform.

ROSIE AT THE TRAIN

(SOUND: Whistle and bells.)

Never mind, stay on, stay on. You're all right. Goodbye. Good-bye. Come back with a little meat on you. If it's only on your elbow. You'll lose it soon enough.

(SOUND: Train starts. Fade gradually.)

Goodbye! Wave, everybody. Wave hard. Goodbye. Goo-bye. Oh, excuse me, Mama, I didn't mean to knock you down. Goodbye. Pick Mama up. Goodbye. Come on, everybody, wave. Wave with one hand while you're getting up, Mama. Never mind, I'm waving double. Look at the old man with the beard. He thinks I'm waving at him. His beard's hanging out of the winder. It's waving right back! Goodbye. That's right, Grandpa, swing it, God love you! Goodbye. Isn't it wonderful! Goodbye. See? I got her on that train without a bit of trouble. Leave these things to me. I know all about trains. I wonder what time she'll get to Syracuse. Porter, what time does that train get to Syracuse? *(Excitement here)* What! It don't go to Syracuse? It's a Florida Train! Mama! She's on the wrong train! Oh, Mama—Essie—Albert—

(Fades.)

HOW TO TRAIN A DOG

A Monologue

By

SYLVIA CLARK

ANNOUNCER. To train a dog, you have to know more than the dog—and so to-night we take you to the living room of our super-psychologist, SYLVIA CLARK!

(*MUSIC:*)

SYLVIA. Now Finney, you've *got* to put that dog in the cellar to-night—he is *not* going to sleep in our room any more—we've had him for three months and it's the same old story every night—"To-morrow we start training him to sleep in the cellar"—well, it's no more of this to-morrow business, it's to-night! Take him to the cellar, Finney—go ahead— Buster! *Buster!* Buster, go with daddy—go on to the cellar— Whajoo say, Finney? You haven't got the heart to do it? You're just the type to spoil him. Now take me—*I'm* for training him to know *I'm* the master—I have the heart and I'm going to put him in the cellar right now! Here Buster—Buster! Come on —follow me—no use cocking your head at me that way, Mr. Win-friends-and-influence-people—I'm wise to you—save the personality tricks—— You're going to stay in the cellar to-night and like it—yes sir—come on, come— *HEY!* Buster! *BUSTER!* Finney! Catch him—he's running under the bed —the bed, Finney—he's under the bed— Look at 'im! *Bus-*

50

tahh, tum out, *Buss-tahh*— Tum on, nice doggie— (*Coughs*)
my, it's dusty under this bed (*Coughs*) Must clean up under
here some day— Buss— (*Coughs*) Finney, get the broom—
we'll poke 'im out from under there— Poke at 'im, Finney—
that's right—poke at 'im—Finney! you're poking at *ME*—it's
the dog we're after, y'know. Here! Give me the broom—I'll get
'im—ugh! Um—he's found a corner where I can't reach him—
Buster! (*Whistles, coughs*) Finney, you whistle—my whistle's
dusty— Come on, Buster—hm—a sit-down strike! I'll tell you
what we'll do— We'll lure 'im— How? With that steak bone
we had left at dinner—go get it, Finney—it's the only way—
That's it— Thanks! Now—I'll just wave it at 'im— Here
Buster-Buster-Buster— (*Aside*) Finney, it's working! You've
gotta use psychology on these dogs, I tell you— Tum on
doggie-woggie-woggie takee nicee bonee— *AH!* There! Now,
mister, I've gotcher and down stairs you go—shut up, Finney!
You act like a sissy-breeches. He's going to the cellar and
that's that— There! Down you go—
Whew! What a struggle! My! Well, I'm glad that's done—
once and for all— (*Sighs*) Whew!
(*Silence for a few seconds.*)
(*In very definite style.*) What? He's barking? I can hear 'im—
so what? Let 'im bark—he'll soon realize he's dealing with a
strong mind and then he will stop barking, I betcha— He'll
know his place is in the cellar and not in our bedroom— You
can't show a trace of weakness either—they know in a minute
—it's gotta be mind over mutt, y'know! Believe me— (*Sighs.*)
(*Silence for a brief spell.*)
Wherejoo put the evening paper, Finney? I haven't seen it,
y'know— (*Yawns*) just wanna read for a few minutes and
then (*Yawns*) oh—I'm sleepy—gonna call it a day soon as
I see what happened to Orphan Annie and Sandy—Ho Yum

Aahn! (*Pause. Beginning to weaken.*) F-i-n-n-ey, djoo notice if there was any water in Buster's pan? You didn't?— Hm— neither did I—hm— (*Pause*). Guess I'll just sneeek over and peeeek down (*Business*) Yep, I'll just-open-the-do— HEY! BUSTER!!! Can you imagine, Finney—he was right behind the door—p-p-p-p-p. Hey, mutt, cut out the kisses—down, Buster! Stop jumping up I tell you—my goodness, I know you're glad to see me—you'd think I'd been away for a million years—p-p-p-p—hey, cut it out—get away—I just wanna see if you have enough water—get over there—get— Finney, will you come here and take a look at this hound? J'ever see such a cute expression? Ha ha—I don't know where he gets 'em—it's a new one on me. Ha ha—cute pup! B-r-r-r, you know, Finney, it feels kinda cold down here, doesn't it? yeah— Bet it's pretty dark and lonely with the kitchen door closed— I—er—kinda—er—think it's a little too cold to train Buster to-night, don't you? Sure! We ought to wait till the weather gets warmer—after all, you can't break the spirits of these kind of dogs—just make mollykyoodles out of them— Guess he'd better sleep in our room to-night— Huh? Sure! Come on, Buster—come on, Boy—ha ha—it's seepybye time— ha ha! The old cellar is no place for man's best friend—no indeedy—

(*FADES: Chattering.*)

RED CARNATIONS

By

GLENN HUGHES

CAST

A MIDDLE-AGED MAN
A YOUNG MAN
A GIRL

RED CARNATIONS

(*MUSIC: Light, modern, of the sweet variety . . . up and fade behind. . . .*)

ANNOUNCER. The ―――― Players present "Red Carnations," a comedy in one act by Glenn Hughes. We are looking down on a secluded corner in a city park about four o'clock of a bright afternoon. A path makes a gradual sweeping curve across the scene and there is a bench about center. A middle-aged, prosperous looking man is seated at one end of the bench. He is wearing a red carnation and is softly and not too accurately whistling a popular tune.

(*MUSIC: Up and out to:*)

MAN (*whistling*).

(*After a few seconds whistling fades to:*)

ANNOUNCER. The Man's attention is attracted by a whistling not his own. He stops and sees a young man approaching with brisk, confident steps along the path. He is well dressed and also wears a red carnation in his lapel.

MAN (*whistling in full*).

(*Whistling stops abruptly and is taken up by:*)

YOUNG MAN (*whistling remote and approaching*).

MAN (*to himself*). Mmm. He's whistling the same thing I am. And wearing a red carnation too.

Y.M. (*whistling, nearly in full, wavers and trails off*).

MAN (*pleasantly*). Good afternoon. Nice day for a stroll in the park.

Y.M. (*none too friendly and slightly remote from the micro-*

55

phone. His voice should be in this position on the microphone until he sits). Good afternoon. Yes.

MAN. Yes. (*Slight pause*) Might as well sit down. Plenty of room on the bench.

Y.M. I beg your pardon.

MAN. I say there's plenty of room.

Y.M. Oh, thanks. Thanks very much. I don't mind standing. It will only be for a minute or two.

MAN. You're not expecting to meet a woman, then?

Y.M. Well . . . why, yes, as a matter of fact, I am.

MAN. You're an optimist.

Y.M. Pardon me?

MAN. I merely remarked that you were an optimist.

Y.M. I'm afraid I don't understand.

MAN. No; but you will later on, when your one or two minutes have turned into one or two hours. I see you don't know very much about the feminine sex.

Y.M. Perhaps not. On the other hand, it strikes me that your remarks are rather personal.

MAN. Well, the only remarks worth making *are* personal. (*Slight pause*) However, if you prefer talking about the weather. . . .

Y.M. I . . . ah, yes, quite right. I am sorry. I was thinking of something else.

MAN. So I perceive. You were looking at your watch. She is already five minutes late.

Y.M. How did you know that?

MAN. Experience. Experience. Romance is like history; it repeats itself. Besides, I am in the same boat with you. My appointment was for five minutes ago, also. The only difference is that I am not worrying about it, and you are.

Y.M. (*fades in to full on this speech*). I think I will sit down if you don't mind. (*Sits*) It's a devil of a bore standing first on one foot and then on the other.

MAN. Have a cigar?

Y.M. No, thanks; I have a cigarette.

MAN. Here's a match.

Y.M. Thanks.

(*SOUND: Striking match.*)

Y.M. Er . . . I . . .

MAN. I beg your pardon?

Y.M. (*annoyed*). Do you always wear a carnation?

MAN. No, not always. Just occasionally.

Y.M. I see.

MAN. You have a very pretty one there.

Y.M. Thanks.

MAN. I say, you're not going to throw it away!

Y.M. I . . . no . . . no I won't.

MAN. They are very pretty flowers. Wonderful fragrance they have too. I'm very fond of them.

Y.M. (*disturbed*). Yes, indeed. A very fine flower. But I . . . well, I hope you won't think me silly, but as a matter of fact, if it doesn't make any difference to you, would you mind keeping your carnation out of sight for a while, until . . .

MAN. Why?

Y.M. Well—just to be a good sport. If you would hide it for a few minutes, I'd be very grateful.

MAN (*good-naturedly*). Now, I'd like nothing better than to do you a favor, Mr. . . . Mr. . . .

Y.M. Smith.

MAN. Thank you. Mr. Smith? That's strange. Very strange.

Y.M. What is strange? The name of Smith?

MAN. Yes, strange that you should have it, when that is my name, too.

Y.M. Oh, your name is Smith, too? Well, after all, there are lots of us in the world . . . lots of us Smiths, I mean . . . so there is no reason why such a coincidence . . .

Man. Of course not, of course not . . . only, I was thinking about the red carnations.

Y.M. Well, I don't see . . .

Man. I may be mistaken, of course. But two Smiths, meeting in the same spot at the same hour, both wearing red carnations! You must confess it's a bit . . .

Y.M. By Jove! So it is!

Man. Yes.

Y.M. (*annoyed*). I wish you could move to another spot, or take that flower out of your lapel, or . . . It isn't absolutely necessary for you to wear it, is it?

Man. But it is! Absolutely! And you are going to cause me all sorts of trouble if *you* don't move, or change your name, or at least throw away your carnation.

Y.M. I shall do nothing of the kind. I can't! My Lord, man, she doesn't know me! That is, she doesn't know what I look like. That is why she asked me to wear a red carnation.

Man. But that is exactly my predicament. The woman *I* am to meet does not know *me* by sight. She asked *me* to wear a red carnation. So you see, I can't help you out. After all, a man must look to his own affairs first.

Y.M. What a beastly coincidence!

Man. Quite!

Y.M. (*brightening*). Oh, well, it may not matter. One of them will arrive before the other does. If you recognize her as your —ah . . . friend . . . you can speak up at once, and get out of the way. If mine should arrive first, I shall do the same.

Man. Hmmm! You know your—ah . . . *friend* . . . when you see her, do you?

Y.M. (*startled*). Why . . . well . . . in a way. That is, her eyes. I would know her eyes anywhere.

MAN. Her eyes! Good heavens!

Y.M. Well, when a woman is in costume and wears a mask . . .

MAN. In costume, and masked!

Y.M. Certainly. Why not? I met her at a masked ball.

MAN. This is uncanny! Positively uncanny! What kind of costume did she wear?

Y.M. She was dressed as the Queen of Sheba.

MAN. The Queen of . . . !

Y.M. What's the matter?

MAN (*trying to recover*). Nothing! Nothing. (*To himself*) I won't believe it. It's impossible!

Y.M. What is impossible?

MAN. Nothing is impossible. . . .

Y.M. Shh. Look there. Coming down the path.

MAN. A girl.

Y.M. A beautiful girl.

MAN. Quite!

Y.M. (*whisper*). Speak to her.

MAN (*whisper*). Who, me?

Y.M. (*whisper*). Which one of us did she look at?

(*Following speeches taken sotto voce increasing to full.*)

MAN. Don't let her get away.

Y.M. She stopped!

MAN. Is she . . . ?

Y.M. I think so. But confound it! I couldn't see her eyes.

MAN. I am certain she is my friend.

Y.M. What! You are?

MAN. From the way she holds her head.

Y.M. If I could only get a glimpse of her eyes!

MAN. The only way to settle it is to call her by name. I suggest you try first.

Y.M. I don't know her name!

MAN. You mean . . .

Y.M. She wouldn't tell me her name. I wish she would quit powdering her nose and turn around.

MAN. This grows more and more unbelievable. I don't know the name of the one I was to meet, either.

Y.M. Good heavens!

MAN. This is awful!

Y.M. We can't stand around all day debating the question. One of us must go ahead and break the ice. If he is wrong, then the other can try.

MAN. A good solution. You should have the privilege of trying it out first. I shall wait here where I can keep an eye on you though. Good luck to you.

Y.M. Thanks. But what the deuce am I to say to her?

MAN. Ask her if you are the man she expected to meet here!

Y.M. But what if she doesn't know?

MAN. That is her worry. You can at least give her a chance to claim you.

Y.M. But she might make a mistake!

MAN. Oh, Lord! Are you going or aren't you?

Y.M. (*fading out*). Yes . . . I'm going. (*Pause, then* Y.M., *remote, clears throat and speaks.*) Er . . . How do you do!

GIRL (*in full, sweetly*). How do you do?

Y.M. (*fading in*). I beg your pardon, but were you . . . I mean . . . I was expecting to meet someone here, and . . . I was wondering . . .

GIRL. Yes, I noticed you were wondering.

Y.M. (*disconcerted*). I suppose you think I am an idiot, but you see . . . well, with both of us wearing red carnations . . .

GIRL. I think they are quite becoming.

Y.M. (*embarrassed*). Thanks, very much, but . . . Well, that isn't exactly the point. (*He laughs nervously.*)

GIRL (*laughing with him*). No, I suppose it isn't.

Y.M. It's awfully difficult to explain.

GIRL (*sympathetically*). Yes, isn't it? (*She laughs again prettily.*)

Y.M. Of course, if you really are the *one* . . . that is, the one I was to meet here, then, maybe you will understand. Do you?

GIRL. No; I don't think I do.

Y.M. (*crestfallen*). Oh! Then, I suppose you aren't the one?

GIRL. The one . . . what?

Y.M. The one . . . I was to meet. Are you?

GIRL. Why, I'm sure I don't know.

Y.M. (*brightening*). Then you *were* to meet someone?

GIRL. Oh, yes.

Y.M. That helps some. And would you know him if you were to see him?

GIRL (*shyly*). I'm afraid not. That is why I asked him to wear a red carnation.

Y.M. Ah! That much is settled. But, of course, *he* is wearing a red carnation too.

GIRL. Yes. That does make it rather complicated, doesn't it?

Y.M. Rather! So, you see, we'll have to think of some other way to identify him.

GIRL. Identify which? You or him?

Y.M. Me! No, not necessarily. Either one. The one you were intending to meet.

GIRL. That's it! We must identify the one I was intending to meet.

Y.M. Can't you think of some way?

GIRL. I can ask your name?

Y.M. Splendid. Go ahead and ask me.

GIRL. Well, then, is your name Smith?

Y.M. (*eagerly*). Yes!

MAN (*remote*). So is mine!

Y.M. Oh, you see, that is another trouble I . . .

GIRL. Is his name Smith too?

Y.M. That's the point. (*Excitedly*) If his name wasn't Smith there wouldn't be any difficulty at all.

GIRL. But how do you know *you* aren't the one to blame?

MAN (*fading in*). It's all a question of who is the original Smith.

Y.M. The original Smith in this instance is the one who had the appointment with Miss . . . I beg your pardon, but you never told me your name.

GIRL. No; I didn't, did I? I am not sure that I ever told *you* anything. Perhaps it was *he* that I talked with.

Y.M. Where? When?

MAN. At the masked ball Friday night.

Y.M. You were there too!

GIRL. He had as much right to be there as you had.

MAN. Certainly.

Y.M. I refuse to stand here all day being made a fool of.

MAN. If you feel that way, you should leave at once.

Y.M. I shan't leave. Don't think you can get rid of me as easily as that. Look at him. How could you mistake him for me?

GIRL. But you were both in costume and wore masks.

MAN. Quite true.

Y.M. But costumes aren't all alike. I was dressed as a *sheik!*

MAN. So was I!

Y.M. What! I don't believe it.

MAN. So far as I know, no one has a patent on the idea.

GIRL. I distinctly remember noticing more than one sheik at the ball.

Y.M. And I suppose you talked to every sheik you saw?

GIRL. It would be very easy to mistake one sheik for another.

Y.M. (*sarcastically*). You invited every sheik you talked with to meet you here in this corner of the park at four o'clock and to wear a red carnation in his coat lapel?

GIRL (*with spirit*). I did no such thing. He was the one who asked *me* to meet him.

MAN. That's right. I asked her to meet me here today.

Y.M. But so did I!

GIRL. How do you know that one of you didn't ask some other girl?

Y.M. Weren't you dressed like the Queen of Sheba?

GIRL. Yes.

MAN. That's how she caught my eye.

Y.M. How do you know there wasn't another Queen of Sheba at the ball?

MAN. The point is, my dear young man, that there is only *one* Queen of Sheba *here*.

Y.M. It means that she has made fools of us both.

MAN. What do you mean?

Y.M. We both made the same proposals to her and she accepted us both.

GIRL. I thought you were the same man.

Y.M. (*to the* MAN, *drily*). She thought we were the same man.

GIRL. I am sorry. I thought you were a little absent-minded perhaps. But in the excitement . . . and the music . . . I must have . . . well, I'm sorry.

Y.M. Oh, we realize that.

GIRL. I suppose the question is now: what to do about it?

MAN. We might flip coins to see which of us stays.

Y.M. If I leave, it will be at the request of the lady.

MAN. Well . . . what does the lady say?

GIRL. If I were to ask you to leave, would you go?

Y.M. Yes. But I would find you again sometime. And when I do, I'll make sure there isn't any other Smith around to interfere.

MAN. What an unkind remark to make!

GIRL. But there would be another Smith around. *My* name is Smith too.

Y.M. What!

GIRL. That's why I remembered your names so easily.

Y.M. I'm through. I've been wasting my time with a pair of lunatics. (*Fading*) Goodby, Mr. Smith . . . and Miss Smith.

GIRL. Oh, don't go. Father! Stop him, please.

Y.M. (*remote*). What was that?

GIRL. Father, don't stand there like a stick!

MAN. Well, I . . . really my dear, I think I've done my part. . . .

Y.M. (*fading in*). What does this mean? Who *are* you, and who is that man?

GIRL (*penitently*). I am Miss Smith, and he is . . . Mr. Smith.

Y.M. (*sternly*). He is your father?

GIRL. Yes. Where are you going?

Y.M. (*remote*). I'm . . . of all . . .

GIRL (*fading in*). Are you awfully mad? (*Pause*) You wouldn't want me to meet strange men in the park without a chaperon. (*Pause*) Even the Queen of Sheba must use discretion.

Y.M. You little devil! I could strangle you!

GIRL. Ohh. (*Pause*) Help! Father, he kissed me!

MAN (*fading in*). Serves you right. Bring him home to dinner with us and maybe he'll kiss you again. Mr. Smith, will you dine with Miss Smith and myself?

Y.M. (*gaily*). Delighted, Mr. Smith. But wait. Aren't you taking a chance? You don't know a thing about me.

RED CARNATIONS

MAN. My boy, I've known your father for twenty years and I've seen you with him. And even if I hadn't, I'd have known you; you're a dead ringer for him.

GIRL. How perfect it all is!

Y.M. Well, I'll be . . .

MAN. Yes, we'll all be late for dinner.

Y.M. Miss Smith, will you take my arm?

GIRL. Delighted, Mr. Smith!

(*MUSIC: Up.*)

PRODUCTION NOTES

This script has been prepared with a minimum of sound effects to simplify production. The sound of the Young Man's footsteps may be added at the opening of the play. They should fade in at a brisk rate, slow down, and come to stop. The steps should be fairly audible behind the last sentence of the Announcer's second speech and there should be a word in the first announcement to describe the walk and help the audience to identify the sound. This could be "gravel," "dirt" or "paved." The same effect could be used at the entrance of the Girl. Her steps would, of course, register at a different cadence.

THE PURLOINED LETTER

By

CHARLTON ANDREWS

(Adapted for the Radio from the Edgar Allan Poe story of the same name)

CAST

AUGUSTE DUPIN, *private detective*
CHARLES DURAC, *his friend*
THE PRIME MINISTER, (*Baron de Monec*)
THE PREFECT OF POLICE, (*M. de Grenel*)
A SERVANT, (*Antoine*)
THE NARRATOR

THE PURLOINED LETTER

NARRATOR. Edgar Allan Poe has often been called the father of the detective story. All of our numberless modern sleuthhounds, with Sherlock Holmes at their head, trace their ancestry back to the Auguste Dupin whom Poe conceived, the private detective who so readily solved the mysteries which had baffled the police of Paris.

We see Dupin now—one summer evening long years ago—smoking his pipe in his little library. With him is his faithful friend Durac.

DURAC. A marvellous example of deduction, Dupin—that case of the murders in the Rue Morgue. And I'm sure the Prefect of Police shares my opinion—though it irks him to acknowledge that any man surpasses him in the field of detection.

DUPIN. Nevertheless, he's coming here this evening to ask me to help him out of another difficulty.

DURAC. The Prefect of Police coming here?

(SOUND: Knock.)

DUPIN. More than likely there he is now.

(SOUND: Door opens.)

SERVANT. Monsieur the Prefect of Police.

DUPIN. You see?—my dear Grenel! Welcome to my den.

PREFECT. How *are* you, Dupin?

DUPIN. You know my friend Durac?

PREFECT. Good evening.

DURAC. Monsieur.

69

DUPIN. Sit down, Grenel, and tell me why I'm honored with this visit.

PREFECT. It's a matter of the greatest secrecy—

DURAC. I was just leaving.

DUPIN. Stay where you are.—Grenel, you can trust Durac as you trust me.

PREFECT. All right, here's the situation. No less a nobleman than the Prime Minister has purloined from an exalted personage a letter of the utmost importance.

DUPIN. And the letter gives the minister a hold on the personage—?

PREFECT. For three months the minister has been wielding this power—

DUPIN. I wondered why the King's brother made such a complete right-about-face.

PREFECT. Eh?—Well, you've guessed it. It *is* the King's brother. And every day he's more convinced of the necessity of reclaiming his letter. But this, of course, can't be done openly.

DUPIN. Naturally.

DURAC. The letter is, no doubt, still with the minister—because it's the possession, and not any employment of the letter, which bestows the power.

PREFECT. The whole theory of *blackmail*. And so, I've searched the minister's house—

DUPIN. Without letting him know it.

PREFECT. Of course. It would be fatal for him to suspect. He's frequently away from home all night. His few servants sleep at a distance from their master's apartment. I have keys which will open any door in Paris. For three months I've spent the greater part of every night, personally, in ransacking the Prime Minister's residence.

DUPIN. Three months! What diligence!

DURAC. Couldn't the Prime Minister have hidden the letter somewhere else than on his own premises?

DUPIN. The peculiar intrigues in which the Prime Minister is involved make the instant availability of the document equally important with its possession.

DURAC. Then, the paper must be on the premises. Surely the minister would not carry it on his own person.

PREFECT. He has been twice waylaid, as if by footpads, and thoroughly searched under my own inspection.

DURAC. Tell us how you searched his house.

PREFECT. I took the building room by room, devoting the nights of a whole week to each. We examined first the furniture. We opened every possible drawer. The cushions of the chairs we probed with fine long needles. We took off the table tops.

DURAC. But why?

PREFECT. Sometimes the top of a table is removed, a leg is bored, an article is deposited in the cavity, and the top is replaced.

DURAC. Couldn't the cavity be detected by sounding?

PREFECT. Not if cotton wadding is placed around the article. Besides, we had to proceed without noise.

DURAC. A letter can be rolled up till it's the size and shape of a knitting needle. Then it could be put into the rung of a chair. Surely you didn't unjoint all the chairs?

PREFECT. We did better. We examined the rungs, and the joint-ings of every description, with a powerful microscope. A sin-gle grain of gimlet-dust would have been as obvious as an apple. Any disorder in the glueing—any gaping of the joints—

DUPIN. You looked into the pictures and mirrors? The beds and bedding? The curtains and carpets?

PREFECT. Yes, and when we had gone over the furniture we examined the house itself. With the microscope we scrutinized each individual square inch—including the two houses immediately adjoining.

Dupin. You looked at the grounds about the houses?

Prefect. All the grounds are paved with brick. We examined the moss between the bricks, and found it undisturbed.

Dupin. As for the minister's papers—?

Prefect. We opened every package and parcel. We turned over every leaf in each volume. With the micrometer we measured the thickness of every book-*cover*. Some five or six volumes, just from the hands of the binder, we carefully probed with the needles.

Dupin. As for the floors?

Prefect. We took up every carpet and microscopically examined the boards.

Dupin. And the paper on the walls?

Prefect. Yes.

Durac. You looked into the cellars?

Prefect. We did.

Durac. Then, the letter is *not* upon the premises.

Prefect. I'm afraid you're right, Durac.—Well, Dupin, what would you advise me to do?

Dupin. I'd advise you to search the premises again.

Prefect. I will—although I'm positive the letter is not there.

Dupin. What was the letter like?

Prefect. It was written on one side of a regulation sheet of white paper. It was folded in the usual way, addressed on the blank side, and fastened with a plain bit of red sealing-wax. It had become more or less soiled from handling. I'm afraid I'll never lay eyes on it.

Dupin. Don't despair. Come back here day after tomorrow. I'll have some sort of news of your purloined letter.

PREFECT. I only hope you're not overestimating your ability. Good evening, gentlemen.

DURAC. Good evening, Monsieur Grenel.

(*SOUND: Door opened.*)

DUPIN. It's been a pleasure to see you. Antoine will show you out—

(*SOUND: Door closed.*)

DURAC. So—what do you mean to do?

DUPIN. Find the letter.

DURAC. Yes, but how?

DUPIN. That will take a bit of thinking.

DURAC. I should say so!

DUPIN. By the way, look in the drawer there and see if you can find my colored spectacles. The Prime Minister and I are both lovers of rare books. I'm going to drop in on him for a few minutes tomorrow.

(*MUSIC: Up, in and out.*)

NARRATOR. It was late the following afternoon when Dupin, returning home, found his friend Durac awaiting him.

(*SOUND: Door opened.*)

DUPIN. Oh, there you are, old chap.

(*SOUND: Door closed.*)

DURAC. Dupin, did you call on the Prime Minister?

DUPIN. I did. He gave me half an hour of his valuable time. I'm going to make another call on him early tomorrow morning. You must come with me—

DURAC. But I—

DUPIN. Oh, you won't have to go in. You'll wait outside for five minutes, and then—by the way, do you own a pistol?

DURAC. Dupin, you know I don't.

DUPIN. In that case, I'll lend you one.

DURAC. A pistol?

DUPIN. Don't be afraid, Durac; there'll be no bullet in it—only a bit of gunpowder.

DURAC. But what am I to do with it?

DUPIN. I'll tell you that a little later.

(*MUSIC: Up, in, and out.*)

THE NARRATOR. Early the following morning Dupin found the industrious Prime Minister at work at his office desk.

DUPIN. Forgive the intrusion, your Excellency—

PRIME MINISTER. It's a pleasure, Dupin, I assure you.

DUPIN. Yesterday afternoon I forgot to tell you about that first edition of Racine's "Phedre" that I ran across last week in the Rue Saint-Honoré.

PRIME MINISTER. I must get it at once. I'm about to have breakfast here in my office. Won't you join me?

DUPIN. No, thanks. My time is limited. Convenient place you have here.

PRIME MINISTER. A simple workroom.

DUPIN. But beautifully appointed. Your great mahogany desk —with its inkstand and its collection of quills. Letter paper—sand-box—sealing wax—a rack for your pipes. Another for visiting cards. A gold-handled paper-knife—

(*Shot, off.*)

PRIME MINISTER (*startled*). What was that?

DUPIN. Sounded like a shot.

PRIME MINISTER. I'll open the window— (*Voice trails off.*)

(*SOUND: Casement opened. Distant cries.*)

DUPIN. Nothing serious, I hope?

PRIME MINISTER (*at a distance*). I can't make it out. A handful of people. Well, nobody seems to be hurt.

(*SOUND: Voices die out, with sound of casement closing.*)

DUPIN. Hardly worth disturbing one's self—

THE PURLOINED LETTER

PRIME MINISTER. At least, it didn't interest *you* enough to draw you to the window.

DUPIN. I felt sure it meant nothing. Well, I must be going. My errand's finished—and I have other work to do.

PRIME MINISTER. You still dabble in detection?

DUPIN. Now and then.

(*SOUND: Door opens.*)

PRIME MINISTER. Do you succeed in every case?

DUPIN. Not always. Still, you'd be surprised at the results I sometimes get.

PRIME MINISTER. Would I, really?

DUPIN. Yes, your Excellency. You'd be very much surprised.

(*SOUND: Door closed. They laugh, going away.*)

(*MUSIC: Up, in, and out.*)

NARRATOR. A short time later Dupin returned home to his anxious friend Durac.

DURAC. Dupin! You're out of breath.

DUPIN. No wonder—with the Prefect of Police on my heels.

DURAC. The Prefect—?

DUPIN. He was just rounding the corner, as I came into the house.

DURAC. Is he after me for firing off that pistol?

DUPIN. No, no, old fellow. I sent for him.

(*SOUND: Distant knocking. Door opened.*)

DUPIN. Antoine, that will be Monsieur de Grenel. Show him in.

SERVANT (*in distance*). Very good, sir.

DURAC. What have you got to tell him?

DUPIN. I promised him news of the purloined letter.

SERVANT. Monsieur the Prefect of Police.

PREFECT. Good morning, gentlemen.

DURAC. Monsieur.

DUPIN. You came quickly, Grenel.

PREFECT. I waste no time.

DUPIN. I should think not—a methodical man like you. Have you searched the Prime Minister's house again?

PREFECT. From top to bottom—without result.

DUPIN. What a pity.

PREFECT. I suppose by now you're convinced there's no such thing as overreaching this clever man.

DUPIN. H'm. Er—how much was the reward offered, did you say?

PREFECT. I didn't say. But I'd give a hundred thousand francs for that letter.

DUPIN. In that case you may as well write me out a check for that amount.

PREFECT. What!

DUPIN. Here's a blank check. Your hand trembles. But no wonder—when you're disposing of a hundred thousand francs. Let me see. Yes, that's right. And here's the purloined letter.

PREFECT (*tremulous*). The letter? You're not fooling me?

DUPIN. Look it over.

PREFECT. Great day! Dupin, how in the world did you get hold of this thing?

DUPIN (*laughs*). To know that will cost you more money.

PREFECT. Eh?

DUPIN. One hundred thousand francs for the letter. Another hundred thousand for telling you how I got it.

PREFECT. A hundred—? It's worth it! But I must hurry to the palace.

(*SOUND: Door opened.*)

DUPIN. Good day, my friend. Drop in another time when you have that baffled feeling.

(*SOUND: Door slam. DUPIN laughs.*)

THE PURLOINED LETTER

DURAC. Dupin, how in the world did you do it?

DUPIN. This Prefect of Police is an ingenious man. But he has never learned to identify his own mind with that of his opponent.

DURAC. I don't understand.

DUPIN. When you're hunting for something that somebody else has hidden, you must try to think how the other fellow would hide it—not how crooks in the mass would hide things.

DURAC. Just what does that mean?

DUPIN. Only *ordinary* minds hide things in ordinary places. If the Prime Minister were an ordinary man, this purloined letter would have been found weeks ago. But he knows that the most remote corner of his house is accessible to the Paris police. Meanwhile it has not occurred to the Prefect that things escape observation by dint of being excessively obvious. He never once thought that the Minister would have deposited the letter beneath the nose of the whole world, as the best way of preventing the world from seeing it.

DURAC. You mean that's what the Minister did?

DUPIN. To conceal the purloined letter, the Prime Minister resorted to the wise expedient of not trying to conceal it at all.

DURAC. But how did you find it?

DUPIN. I put on my colored goggles, pretending that my eyes were weak, and called on the minister. While we were conversing, I studied his office intently. After a time my glance rested on a trumpery card-rack, hanging from the middle of the mantelpiece. In it were several visiting cards and a solitary letter.

DURAC. *The* letter?

DUPIN. It was soiled and crumpled—torn nearly in two, as if it had been considered worthless. It had a large black seal, bearing the Prime Minister's crest. It was addressed in a feminine hand to the Minister himself. At once I felt sure it was the letter I was looking for.

DURAC. It would have been dangerous to take it then.

DUPIN. Decidedly. So I memorized the appearance of the letter, went home, and reproduced it as faithfully as I could. It was clear that the original letter had been turned, as a glove, inside out, redirected, and resealed. Next morning, when I called on the minister again, and you had distracted his attention by firing that shot, I substituted my facsimile letter for the one in the card-rack.

DURAC. You were playing safe.

DUPIN. I was. Anyhow, I sympathize with the King's brother, who has been for so long in the Prime Minister's power. Now I have reversed the situation. Unaware that the letter is gone, the minister will continue his exactions and so bring about his own destruction. And when he opens the letter I left in his card-rack, he'll find a very amusing little valentine. I spent half an hour last night, composing it.

(*MUSIC: Up.*)

THE GOLDEN AGE
By
MONTE KLEBAN

CAST

LAURA
GEORGE
LUCILLE
YOUNG MAN
SUSAN

THE GOLDEN AGE

ANNOUNCER. And now we bring you, The Golden Age.
(*MUSIC: Light, homey number. End by synchronizing with:*)
(*SOUND: Chimes of clock striking ten.*)
GEORGE (*grumpily*). H'm. Ten o'clock and Lucille not home yet.
LAURA. Now, dear, stop fretting. Lucille can take care of herself.
GEORGE. Well, I don't like the idea of my daughter traipsing around 'til all hours of the night.
LAURA (*indulgently*). Oh, dear! All hours of the night! Why, it's only ten o'clock.
GEORGE (*persistently*). It's after ten. She's too young to be out alone.
LAURA. I suppose you think Lucille just stopped getting older when she was a child. You forget she's nineteen. And, besides, she's not alone. She's with two of her girl friends—
(*SOUND: Door opens in distance.*)
LAURA. There she is now.
LUCILLE (*Calls from distance*). Good night. And—and thank you.
(*SOUND: Door closes.*)
LAURA (*calls*). We're in here, Lucille.
LUCILLE (*fade in*). I'm coming. Hello, Mother, Dad. Whew— what a day.
GEORGE (*severely*). Do you know that it's after ten, Lucille?

81

LUCILLE. Is it, Daddy? I didn't realize—you see, we went to the beach—

LAURA. To the beach? The three of you— I mean, just you girls?

LUCILLE. Why, yes. It was glorious. Oh—I feel so fresh and—salty.

GEORGE. Swimming?

LUCILLE. Yes—the water was so cool—so— (*Suddenly*) Mother?

LAURA. Yes, dear?

LUCILLE. Mother, I'd—I'd—like to—well—

GEORGE (*irritated*). Speak up, Lucille. What is it?

LUCILLE (*blurts*). Well, I'd like to bring someone here for dinner some night next week.

LAURA. Why, of course, dear. You know we always like to have the girls in.

LUCILLE. But—but this isn't a girl. It's a—a man.

GEORGE (*incredulously*). A man?

LAURA (*puzzled*). A man?

LUCILLE (*confused*). Yes. You see, I just met him—I mean—at the beach—and—

GEORGE (*suspiciously*). Met him at the beach. H'm. Who is he? Who introduced you?

LAURA. Do we know his family, dear?

LUCILLE. Well, you see, he doesn't come from here—I mean—

GEORGE. Who introduced you?

LUCILLE. No one—that is— I suppose you could say the sun and the sand and the water—and maybe even a little giggle when he tripped and fell over my beach bag introduced us. But he's so nice. Please. I know it's—

GEORGE (*pompously*). Now see here, Lucille, I have something to say about this. You may be young and modern, and every other dash blamed thing young people are nowadays—but

I will not have my daughter picking up with strange men. That's final.

LAURA. Now, darling, don't excite yourself. Remember your indigestion.

GEORGE (*heatedly*). Blast my indigestion! I told you no good would come of letting her run around until all hours of the night. Now she wants to bring home a—a—beach comber!

LUCILLE (*hurt*). Please, Daddy. He's not a beach comber. He's young and he's an engineer and he—

GEORGE (*explodes*). I don't care what he is. I'm not going to have my home cluttered up with—with—riff-raff.

LAURA. Please don't shout like that. I can just see another indigestion spell coming on.

LUCILLE (*pleads*). Daddy, I'm sure you'll like him. I'm sure you will.

GEORGE (*roars*). No! (*Hiccoughs*) No! You can't bring him here! (*Hiccoughs*) Now look at me. (*Hiccoughs*) Indigestion. All on account of a— (*Hiccoughs*) —of a beach comber. I'm going to— (*Hiccoughs*) to bed. Laura, are you coming?

LAURA. I'll be right along. Don't forget to take some bicarb.

GEORGE. Bah!

(*SOUND: Scraping of chair on floor, heavy, stamping footsteps, slam of door.*)

LUCILLE. (*tearfully*). Oh, Mother, what am I going to do? You see, it was his idea. He wanted to—to meet you and Daddy.

LAURA (*kindly*). Has it gone as far as that, dear?

LUCILLE (*breaks down*). Yes—oh, Mother—I'm so—happy. And so—so miserable.

LAURA (*soothingly*). Now, dear. I know how you feel. But perhaps I know your dad a little better than you do. Here, sit down on this footstool. There. Let me tell you a little—well something that happened to me, dear, just when I was about your age. We had beaches, too, in those days, you know. Well, one Sunday, your Aunt Susan and I were at the beach—

(*FADE.*)

(*SOUND: fade in beach noises.*)

SUSAN. Laura, this sun is giving me a slight headache. I'm going up to the pavilion to sit in the shade.

LAURA (*a much younger and more spirited* LAURA). All right, Susan. I'll be up after a while.

SUSAN (*seriously*). Now don't you let any of these slickers flirt with you.

LAURA. Oh, silly. Twenty-three skidoo.

SUSAN (*primly*). All right, Laura. But mind what I told you. I'll be waiting in the pavilion.

LAURA (*sings softly*). On a Sunday afternoon— In the merry month of June— Take a trip up the Hudson or down the bay—oh!

(*This exclamation is brought on by someone tripping over her parasol.*)

(*Following few lines are simultaneous.*)

YOUNG MAN. Golly, I'm sorry, Miss—

LAURA. Did you hurt yourself?

YOUNG MAN. Did I hurt you?

LAURA. Are you all right?

(*Both laugh.*)

YOUNG MAN. Gosh, I'm a clumsy oaf. I hope I didn't break your parasol.

LAURA (*giggles*). No, my parasol is all right—but you— (*Giggles*) you— (*Laughs uncontrollably.*)

YOUNG MAN (*puzzled*). What's so funny?

LAURA (*gasps between laughs*). The way you fell. Oh—forgive me—you looked so funny— (*Laughs*) Down went McGinty— (*Laughs louder.*)

YOUNG MAN (*chuckles*). I guess I did look funny, falling that way. Down went McGinty. (*Laughs*) Say, that's good!

(*They both give way to unrestrained hilarity.*)

LAURA (*finally quieting a little, but still giggling*). I'm sorry I —laughed at you that way.

YOUNG MAN. Oh, that's all right. I really didn't mean to—drop in so unexpectedly.

LAURA. Well, I'll have to go now—

YOUNG MAN (*unexpectedly vehement*). Oh, no! Don't! I mean —I've just met you and—

LAURA. But you haven't met me. You just—well, you just fell over my parasol.

YOUNG MAN. Sure, but—well, gosh, I mean, I'd like to meet you, but you see, I'm a stranger here myself—and—and—well, who can we get to introduce us?

LAURA (*laughs*). I don't know. But I know it isn't proper for me to be talking to you.

YOUNG MAN. I know! I have it! Here, loan me your parasol. There. See? Now, it's standing up by itself, just like a person. Why, it is a person; it's Sir Percival Parasol. So glad to see you here, dear old friend, Percy. And may I have the pleasure of being introduced to your charming companion?

LAURA (*laughs*). Oh, you are a silly goose. But—but—well, I suppose Sir Percy will do—

YOUNG MAN (*happily*). Oh, that's dandy. What can I call you?

LAURA (*playfully*). Well—as long as I'm with Sir Percy Parasol today, I suppose you can call me—why—Lady Elaine. I've always wanted to play at being—Lady Elaine.

YOUNG MAN. Well, that makes me Sir Launcelot, doesn't it? All right, fair lady, your knight is at your slightest command.

LAURA. Rise, Sir knight, and let's—let's go into the water.

YOUNG MAN. To the water then, my lady.

LAURA (*laughs*). Wait! I forgot Susan.

YOUNG MAN. Forgot Susan? What's a Susan?

LAURA. A Susan happens to be a sister who has a slight head-ache from the sun and is up at the pavilion.

YOUNG MAN (*disappointed*). Oh.

LAURA. You mustn't frown like that. It makes you look like—like a little boy who just lost his lollipop.

YOUNG MAN. That's the way I feel. You won't leave me yet, will you?

LAURA (*lightly*). Um—well, I suppose anything would be better than to have you look like that. Tell you what. I'll tell Susan I've met—the—minister's wife, and to go along without me.

YOUNG MAN (*brightly*). Say, that's just fine! I'll stay here and —and look like the minister's wife.

LAURA. I'll be right back— (*Fade.*)

(*MUSIC: Gay, lilting number behind the following scene.*)

(*SOUND: Washing of waves breaking on beach.*)

YOUNG MAN (*fade in*). Well, you look worried. Did you have any trouble with Susan?

LAURA. No, only that Susan asked me to invite the minister's wife to tea tomorrow.

YOUNG MAN (*playfully*). I'll be delighted. That's very nice of Susan.

LAURA. *You'll* be delighted!

YOUNG MAN. Of course. Don't forget, I'm the minister's wife.

LAURA (*laughs*). Oh—I *did* forget.

YOUNG MAN. Tell you what, let's forget our worries with a dip in the good old briny deep. Ready?

LAURA (*gaily*). All right, here we go!

YOUNG MAN. Better hold on to me. I'll hold on to the ropes.

LAURA. Here comes a big one! Look out!

YOUNG MAN. Take my hand! Here, hang on.

LAURA. Whee! That was a mountain.

YOUNG MAN. Here comes another—look out!

LAURA. This is wonderful. Ooooh!

YOUNG MAN. Had enough?

LAURA. Oh, no. I'm a regular fish. I love the water.

YOUNG MAN. You look more like a mermaid to me. A—a— darned pretty mermaid, too.

LAURA. You'll make me blush.

YOUNG MAN. Look out. Here comes a big wave. Golly, this is fun— (*Fade.*)

(*SOUND: Washing of waves out.*)

(*MUSIC: Bridge, fade in, up, and out.*)

LAURA (*fade in*). Oh, you're all dressed and you got here first!

YOUNG MAN. First? I've been waiting here forever. Ever since I can remember. It must have been years and years. I'm an old, old man.

LAURA. Now, it's not as bad as all that.

YOUNG MAN. Would you—would you like some ice cream? Or a sherbet?

LAURA. Oh, I'd love it.

YOUNG MAN. That's too good to be true. There's a table right over there. Here, let me carry your valise.

LAURA. Sure you can handle it?

YOUNG MAN. Lady Elaine, I could carry a mountain on my back, if you asked me to.

LAURA. Isn't this the loveliest day—?

YOUNG MAN. The loveliest in my whole young life. Here you are. This all right?

LAURA. Yes, fine, thank you.

YOUNG MAN. There's only one thing more that could happen today to make it one I'd never forget. But—well—I suppose you'd think I was fresh if I asked you.

LAURA. Of course I would. (*Laughs*) But go ahead, anyway.

YOUNG MAN. Well, I'd—I'd—I'd— (*Gasps.*)

LAURA. It must be something dreadful—what is it?

YOUNG MAN (*blurts*). I'd like to take you to dinner—to Charlie's Oyster House—and then—then to see the moonlight—with you—from the boardwalk—the moon over the water—

LAURA (*coyly*). Moonlight! You are bold. But how do you know there will be a moon tonight?

YOUNG MAN. That's easy. If the moon ever shone before, it will shine tonight. And if it never shines again, it will still be here tonight.

LAURA. My, a very positive young man. But I'm afraid it's impossible. No, I'm sorry.

YOUNG MAN (*pleads*). Please, just this once, won't you—

LAURA (*interrupts, speaks with finality*). There's no use your coaxing me, I just won't do it— (*Fade.*)

(*MUSIC: Sweet number as background.*)

YOUNG MAN. You're not sorry you came, are you? Just look at that moonlight. It looks like little silver lights dancing on the waves.

LAURA. No, I'm not sorry I came. It is beautiful, isn't it?

YOUNG MAN. You know, I never used to think much about the moon. But, now, here on the boardwalk, with you—it's almost like there's something personal in it. Like it—like it came out just for us.

LAURA. There's one thing I'll say for you. You're a very persuasive young man.

YOUNG MAN. Laura, you remember that song you were singing when I—when I fell into your life?

LAURA. "On A Sunday Afternoon?"

YOUNG MAN. Yes. Would you—would you mind singing it again. Just a little.

LAURA. Oh, I can't sing.

YOUNG MAN. Please!

LAURA (*pleased*). Well—all right. (*Sings.*)

> On a Sunday afternoon—
> In the merry month of June—
> Take a trip up the Hudson or down the Bay,
> Take a trolley to Coney or Rockaway,
> On a Sunday afternoon, you can see the lovers spoon—

(*She stops suddenly.*)

YOUNG MAN. Laura, may I kiss you?

LAURA (*breathes*). Oh—yes!

(*MUSIC: Gay number.*)

LAURA. So you see, Lucille, those things happened to me when I was a girl, too.

LUCILLE. Oh, Mother, that's—that's beautiful. But what—what happened to him?

LAURA. What happened to him? Why, I married him, of course.

LUCILLE (*dazed*). You mean, Daddy is Sir Launcelot—?

LAURA (*sighs*). Yes, but that was long ago. Will Tuesday night be all right to bring your young man to dinner?

(*MUSIC: Crescendo finish.*)

TAXI

By
ALICE C. D. RILEY

CAST

MADGE KIMBERLY
ALEC KIMBERLY

TAXI

(*SOUND: Street noises down town in big city. Full mike then fade behind below.*)

ANNOUNCER. We are down town in a big city. From opposite sides of the street, two persons, a man and a woman, are calling the same taxi simultaneously.

ALEC. ⎱ ⎰ Taxi! Taxi! Hoo-oooo! Taxi!
MADGE. ⎰ ⎱ Hey! Taxi! (*whistles*) Hey!

(*SOUND: Bring up street noises. Taxi braking to curb. Two doors opened. Bags tossed in. Doors slammed shut. Taxi up and away and then behind below. Then fade slowly.*)

MADGE. ⎱ ⎰ Municipal Airport, driver. Hurry!
ALEC. ⎰ ⎱ Airport, driver. And step on it. (*Surprise*) Why—er—MADGE!

MADGE (*surprise*). I—why, Alec! Alec Kimberly, this is my taxi.

ALEC. I called him from across the street.

MADGE. I called him from the sidewalk. He drove right up. I was in first.

ALEC. Nonsense! It doesn't matter.

MADGE. It does. It's my taxi. You get out and take another.

ALEC. Taxis aren't as easy to take as pills. I don't see another.

MADGE. You've no right here. You know very well that if the Judge saw us together in the same taxi he would refuse me my divorce.

ALEC. He won't see us. For the love of Mike, Madge, be reasonable.

MADGE. I am. Get out!

93

ALEC. Just like old times, isn't it, dear?

MADGE. Alec! I'm no longer dear to you.

ALEC. You will be when I start paying alimony.

MADGE. I certainly hope so.

ALEC. Ah! You haven't changed in all the ages—or is it only six months since you left me? You're looking very beautiful, you know.

MADGE. Don't think you can flatter me into coming—

ALEC (*quickly*). No, No! Just the natural response of any man to a lovely woman. A little plumper—to my eye.

MADGE (*indignantly*). I am not. It's this coat. You always said it made me look— What are you laughing at?

ALEC (*laughing*). Your touchy point, eh, Madge? Just the same, you are good for sore eyes.

MADGE. I've heard that before.

ALEC (*change to sharp tone*). From that sissy, Jim Burns, I'll bet.

MADGE (*defensively*). Jimmy has good taste.

ALEC (*savagely*). So I've been told. He throws plenty of compliments your way.

MADGE. At least, he never threw a newspaper at me.

ALEC. Well, who wouldn't! You drove me nuts that morning.

MADGE. You had left the cap off the toothpaste.

ALEC. Oh, yeah? You've done it plenty of times yourself.

MADGE. But it was you who made the shelf all messy.

ALEC (*triumphantly*). Well—it isn't messy now.

MADGE. Alec! You don't mean you've cleaned it?

ALEC. No. I just moved down one shelf.

MADGE. Oh—! That's my powder shelf.

ALEC. Not now it isn't.

MADGE. But Alec—

TAXI

ALEC. I've got the whole bathroom to myself.

MADGE. I'll bet you still leave wet towels all over.

ALEC. Why not? There's no one now to complain.

MADGE. Why, Alec! I believe you're glad I'm gone.

ALEC. Well, it gives me two shelves to myself. Still—er—

MADGE. Yes—what—?

ALEC. I'll give you both shelves and pick up the towels if you'll come back.

MADGE. You'd call me a fussy old maid before the week was out.

ALEC. I won't. I swear I won't. I'll even let the cat sleep in my chair.

MADGE. Oh! How is Belteshazzar?

ALEC. Belteshazzar's had kittens.

MADGE. Belteshazzar! Kittens! Oh! We'll have to give him a new name—

ALEC. A good idea! Come back and we'll talk it over.

MADGE. We will not.—er—Alec—how many kittens?

ALEC. Five. There are only two now.

MADGE. What happened?

ALEC. I paid Gus to take them away.

MADGE. Gus—?

ALEC. You know—our janitor. We still have the same janitor.

MADGE. Does he still get drunk on Saturday nights?

ALEC. Yep. He and Mrs. Stowsky go on binges together. She's our new char-woman.

MADGE. Disgraceful! Why keep her on?

ALEC. I didn't. I discharged her.

MADGE. Good for you! But—er—who gets your breakfast?

ALEC (*defensively*). I get it myself.

MADGE. Heavens! The kitchen must look awful.

ALEC. It does. It needs a woman's hand.

TAXI

MADGE. Not my hand. If you like to live in a mess why should I care?—er—Alec. (*Pleading*) Why won't you take another taxi?

(*SOUND: Fade in sound of motor to squeal of brakes below.*)

ALEC. Because it's nonsense. We're both going to the same place. Why not go on as we are?

MADGE. "Go on as we are!" That's what you said when I first asked for a divorce.

ALEC. Oh, did I?

MADGE. Alec Kimberly, have you forgotten that I'm getting a divorce from you?

ALEC. Is it likely! I've been wondering—

(*SOUND: Squeal of brakes. Stop cab. Motor running behind below.*)

MADGE. Ooooooh!—Driver, what happened?

ALEC. Only a truck. We just missed it. On our way again.

(*SOUND: Taxi starting and fade motor behind below.*)

MADGE. Oh! My hat! He's smashed it.

ALEC. Sorry! Such a pretty hat.

MADGE (*pleased*). Oh! You like it—? —er—I mean—my hand-bag's fallen. Oh dear! It's open. Everything's out.

ALEC. I'll help you. Here's your mirror.—And your handkerchief— (*Sniffs it*) Aaaah! "Dream of Love." The same old scent. Just like old times.

MADGE. You remember—? Oh, Alec!— (*Firmly*) How annoying! It's soiled. Where's my compact?

ALEC. Compact! Oh! Here it is. Say! isn't this the one—?

MADGE. (*softly*). Your last present—Christmas—!

ALEC. Yeah, Christmas. Remember? You thought I'd forgotten—

MADGE. Yes. I was—horrid.

ALEC. You sure were.

MADGE (*hardening*). Beast! I was not. Let's see! Have I found everything? No. My lip-stick—where's my lip-stick?

ALEC. Huh?—I don't see it.

MADGE. But Alec! I mustn't lose it.

ALEC. What's a lip-stick! They're all alike. You can buy another.

MADGE. No, no! It must be this one.

ALEC. Why?

MADGE. Because—I—er—

ALEC. Say! What's this under my heel? Oh! Here it is. Gosh! I've smashed it.

MADGE (*plaintively*). Ooooh! My most precious lip—

ALEC. Say!—Is this the one I bought you in Miami—on our honeymoon?

MADGE. Yes. And rice all over our room—that lovely Butterfly Room. Everyone knew we were bride and groom. Wasn't it perfect!

ALEC (*tenderly*). Madge! Then you still—?

MADGE. Of course I remember. (*Chuckles*) The way you danced on the toes of my best slippers instead of on the floor.

ALEC. I never was strong on dancing.

MADGE. Do you call what you did dancing! Oh, it's hopeless! Then it began—all the annoying little things.—You never did remember to be nice in little things. You always took the best chair by the fire.

ALEC (*amazed*). Why, Madge! That old arm-chair? I never dreamed you wanted it.

MADGE. I didn't. But you never asked me—

ALEC. Well of all the silly ideas—

MADGE. And you wouldn't wear your dress-suit.

ALEC. It got too tight.

MADGE. And you slept through the opera.

ALEC. Oh, well—the opera! Who wouldn't? By the way, Madge, I've something to tell you—

MADGE. I know. That blond. I've heard about her.

ALEC (*blankly*). Blond?

MADGE. Don't play innocent. My dear friends see that I'm told, —the cats!

ALEC. Then you must know they're lying?

MADGE. Oh, Alec!—Do I?

ALEC. Of course you do. They're just playing horse with you. You know I always go east on a business trip—

MADGE. Business! Business!All you think of is money.

ALEC. I have to, to keep you supplied. But not any more.

MADGE. But Alec! I've got to have alimony.

ALEC. Nix. My policy is: Everything for my wife but not one cent for alimony.

MADGE. Why you stingy thing! I'm getting out of this taxi— right now. Driver! Stop!

(*SOUND: Knuckles on glass, knocking.*)

ALEC. Oh, Madge! Use your head. Listen! I've got to tell you something—something important.

MADGE. I won't listen.

ALEC. You've got to listen to this. The judge says we're not divorced.

MADGE. Eh? Not—divorced?

ALEC. No.

MADGE. You mean I've spent all that money for a lawyer, and he's made me stay away from the flat, even when I had the tooth-ache and wanted awfully to come home—to get my electric pad—and I've missed the—I mean—well—the opera and everything? And I'll bet you've gone and bought a new car—?

ALEC. Sure.

MADGE. What color?

ALEC. Red.

MADGE (*groans, says flatly*). Fire-engine red.

ALEC. No. Lip-stick.

MADGE. To ride in a red car! Alec Kimberly, that's the meanest thing you ever did to me.

ALEC. Not my fault—the judge's.

MADGE. How?

ALEC. When he said: "No divorce. Collusion!" Well, I felt like whoopee. Wanted to paint the town, so—I bought a red car.

MADGE. I suppose you think that's funny. Well, I was never so humiliated in all my life. (*Begins to sob*) Oh, dear! I've made such a silly mess of it all.

ALEC (*gently*). Don't cry, Madge. I'll give you plenty. You can have separate maintenance—

MADGE. *SEPARATE!* That's just what's so awful—never having an escort to take me anywhere—

ALEC. No? I heard Jim Burns was taking you around.

MADGE. Oh, that! He's only Jimmy. He's been an angel to me in all my trouble.

ALEC. The deuce he has! I'll break every bone in his body. Look here, Madge, you're still my wife and I won't have any of this Jimmy stuff.

MADGE. Why, all he did was to make my reservations for me.

ALEC. What reservations?

MADGE. You know—at The Miami Hotel—that Butterfly Room.

ALEC. That! Why, that's our honeymoon room. What the heck—? Why should you want to go there?

MADGE. I just have to go there now and then.

ALEC. Why?

MADGE. You wouldn't—understand.

ALEC. Why wouldn't I?

TAXI

MADGE. Because you wouldn't. (*Calls*) Driver! Please hurry! I don't want to miss this plane.

ALEC (*baffled*). O.K. If that's the way you feel about it— (*Calls*) Step on it!

(*SOUND: Motor up and away. Sudden brakes. Wheels skidding. Bump stop. Motor running behind below.*)

MADGE (*stifled cry*). Oooooh! What happened?

ALEC. Why not look? You can't see anything with your face buried in my shoulder.

MADGE. Heavens! What a skid! Pretty nearly the end of us.

ALEC. It was a close shave all right. What is it, Madge? Did you knock your head? Are you hurt?

MADGE (*hysterically*). Oh! I don't know—I don't know—Oh, Alec!

ALEC (*frightened*). Madge, darling! You're hurt. We must get a doctor.

MADGE. No, no! There isn't time. I must make that plane.

ALEC (*suspicious*). Why? Is Jimmy waiting for you?

MADGE. Good gracious, no.

ALEC (*still suspicious*). But—there is a man—?

MADGE (*half laughing*). Oh, yes—yes!

ALEC (*savagely*). I'll break every bone—who is he?

MADGE. Don't you know? It's—YOU.

ALEC. MADGE! Darling! You mean—you and I—again—?

MADGE. Yes. If you want me.

ALEC. Want you! I'll say! Come! Give me a kiss! (*Kiss*) Gee! Lady Luck is sure with me today.

MADGE. Lady Luck?

ALEC. Yes. Throwing us both into the same taxi.

MADGE (*little laugh*). Oh! That! Well—I managed that—with Jimmy's help. He found out your plans and I bribed the— the taxi—

TAXI

ALEC. *DARLING!* I can't believe it. But—these trips you've taken—down to Miami—I don't understand. What in thunder have you done there?

MADGE (*between a laugh and a sob*). Oh! I—I'd go to the Butterfly Room and—just cry my eyes out.

ALEC. Well—of all the crazy—say! I don't see why you—changed—

MADGE. Don't you, my dear? It was that skid decided me. So near to death—! They say that when you're drowning you see all your life before you. Well—I saw mine—without you—alone—lonely—! Oh! I've been such a fool. Alec! Promise you'll never leave me.

(*SOUND: Fade in motor behind below.*)

ALEC. Never, darling! This is a new start. We'll go—

MADGE. To the Butterfly Room.

ALEC. Yes. (*Shouts*) Driver! Step on it! Make it fast!

(*SOUND: Taxi up and away.*)

THE DESERT SHALL REJOICE

By

ROBERT FINCH AND BETTY SMITH

CAST

Buck
Johnny
Curley
Storekeeper
Nick Katapouli
Rosa Katapouli
Dusty
Doctor
Jose
Maria

THE DESERT SHALL REJOICE

(*MUSIC: up. Plays cowboy music. "Git Along Little Dogies" or something similar. Fade on signal to:*)

NARRATOR. Along the wooden sidewalk of the narrow main street of Elkhorn, a little desert town in Nevada, three cowboys are walking, in their high-heeled boots and leather chaps. It is evening.

(*MUSIC: Up, then FADE OUT.* BUCK *continues to hum the cowboy tune, softly, after MUSIC fades.*)

(*SOUND: Jingle of spurs and the slow thumping of boots on the wooden sidewalk.*)

JOHNNY. Look, fellers. Time we was gettin' outta here.

BUCK (*stops humming*). Yeah. We been wanderin' aroun' town all day long and we *still* got most of our money. (*Resumes humming.*)

CURLEY. I tell ya, Buck, there just ain't no place to spend it. No movies, no dance hall, no nothin'. We better start back to the ranch. Whatta you say, Johnny?

JOHNNY. Yeah. Let's git fer home. It's eighteen miles back to the Diamond O and that ain't no little jaunt.

CURLEY. It sure ain't. Not even for the horses. Come on, Buck! Let's hightail fer home.

BUCK. No *sir!* Curley, I ain't a-goin' back to the ranch. Not till I've spent some o' this here cash the boss paid me. I worked for it, now I gotta spend it. Why, Curley, you must be a-gettin' old! Don't enjoy spendin' your money any more.

CURLEY. I'll spend 'er all right, if you'll show me a place.

(*Sighs*) But I'm tired o' walkin' and my feet hurts me somethin' fierce.

JOHNNY. Hey! Wait a minute! Look at that, would ya?

(*SOUND: Sound of boots stops.*)

JOHNNY. Look at all them purty things in thet there store winda! Shore shine with them lights on, don't they?

BUCK. Shore do!

JOHNNY. Them gold things are what ketches my eye. Look at 'em shine! Little gold boxes an' ornaments an' doo-dads an' fandangles! An' the little gold ring.

CURLEY. I like to look at all them sweet-smellin' things, wrapped up in the bright colored paper.

BUCK. Say! I got a idea! Why not us buy a lot of these here things? For presents!?

CURLEY. Who in time'd we give 'em to? Each other? *I* ain't got no fambly to buy presents for. I'm just a pore lone maverick.

JOHNNY. *I* ain't got no fambly, that's sure. We couldn't buy the Boss a present. He'd think we'd went loco, sure enough.

BUCK. Let's buy 'em anyhow. Even if we ain't got any folks to give 'em to. Then we'll *find* somebody that'd like 'em for a present.

JOHNNY. Sure! Let's do! Hurry up! We'll buy a whole flock o' these here things and then we'll start back to the Diamond O.

BUCK. First person we see that'd like to have 'em, we'll give 'em to. Presents from us. Come on in the store.

(*SOUND: Thump of boots as they walk in store. Door opening. Door closing.*)

STOREKEEPER. Good evening, gentlemen. What can I do for you?

BUCK. We wanta look at them things you got in the winda.

CURLEY. We wanta buy 'em . . . fer presents.

STOREKEEPER. Certainly. Step right this way and I'll get them for you.

(*MUSIC: Up. FADE on signal to:*)

NARRATOR. On a winter night in the Nevada desert the sky is a bright, almost Oriental blue. The stars gleam with a glittering brightness above the low, black mountain ranges. Some miles from Elkhorn, on the highway which runs through the desert, is Nick's Place, a small and lonely tourist camp. It is a little cluster of weather-beaten cabins, the largest one of them a combined office, lobby for guests and cafe, standing on a little hill above the highway. The lights are out. DUSTY, a young wayfarer, sits on a stool beside the lunch counter, looking out at the starlight. Nearby is ROSA, NICK'S wife. NICK KATAPOULI himself is standing on the little front porch, gazing up at the sky.

(*MUSIC: Up then fade out.*)

NICK (*shouting excitedly, proudly*). Here she goes! I'm gonna turn 'er on! One! Two! *Three!!*

DUSTY, ROSA *and* NICK. Ah-h-h!

NICK. Come on out an' see it! It's the nicest 'lectric sign I ever saw! It's *beautiful!* Did you ever see anything so beautiful, Rosa?

ROSA. It's nice . . . it makes a pretty light. But Nick . . . it's so big . . . costs so much to run . . . think of the 'lectric bill. . . .

NICK. With a big power line goin' right by the place we'd be crazy not to use the 'lectricity. Ain't that right, Dusty?

DUSTY. Sounds all right to me, Nick.

NICK. There! You see, Rosa? People see that big sign for twenty mile! They all come to Nick's Place. Spend lottsa money.

ROSA. I hope so. . . .

(*SOUND: Footsteps climbing the wooden stairs.*)

DOCTOR. Good evening.

NICK. Hello, Doctor! Whatta you think of my new 'lectric sign?

DOCTOR. I . . . Nick . . . it's magnificent!

NICK. That's just what *I* said. Magnificent. Come on in. Wait'll I turn the lights on inside.

(*SOUND: Turning light switch on.*)

NICK. I turned 'em out so's we see the new sign better. Want some coffee, Doc?

DOCTOR. Thanks.

(*SOUND: Pouring cup of coffee.*)

NICK. I was gonna have a big sign with red an' green an' purple lights. Like this: "The Traveler's Rest. Cabins for Tourists. Nick Katapouli, Proprietor. Cafe In Connection." But the 'lectric man say that cost me three thousand dollars!

ROSA (*ominously*). Nick!

NICK. All right, Rosa! I *see* you! I *see* you roll your eyes aroun' and look mad! . . . I didn't *buy* it! I just bought that big 'lectric star. That alone.

DOCTOR. It's a pretty big star all right, Nick.

NICK. Only twenty feet high. Seven hunderd bulbs. Five hunderd dollars. Believe me, hadda hard time gettin' it up on the roof. I wouldn't 'a' got it so cheap, but the 'lectric man got it second-handed from a busted-down movie house. The Star Picture Palace. Me, I like everything *big*. Big signs, big everything. Rosa says it costs too much. She's mad.

ROSA. You throw away money, Nick. But you a good kind man. I know you well.

NICK (*laughs*). My wife say she know me. Well, maybe all right. An' maybe not, Rosa. More coffee, Doctor?

DOCTOR. No thanks.

NICK. You want some more, Dusty?

Dusty. I still got most o' this cup.

Doctor. Say, Nick . . . I was wondering. The missus and I wanted to have a little celebration, in honor of the day. We brought along a cold chicken. A little bit of wine would make it taste better. I don't suppose . . .

Nick. Say no more!

(SOUND: *Drawer being opened, clink of bottle.*)

Nick. From me to you! A surprise!

Doctor. Say! This *is* a surprise, Nick. I don't know how to thank you.

Nick. Don't even try.

Doctor. Well, I'll get back to the wife. She may be lonesome.

(SOUND: *Stool being pushed back from counter.*)

Nick. Everything OK down at the cabin? Comfortable?

Doctor. Absolutely fine, Nick. Thanks to you.

Nick. If those people in Number Nine Cabin make too much noise you let me know. I tell 'em to shut up.

Doctor. Oh, they won't bother us. Goodnight, Mrs. Katapouli . . . gentlemen . . .

Rosa, Nick, Dusty. G'nite.

Doctor. Merry Christmas.

Nick. Same to you, Doctor.

(SOUND: *Footsteps going downstairs.*)

Nick. He's a nice fella.

Dusty. Sure he is.

(SOUND: *Clatter of coffee cup being set hastily in saucer.*)

Dusty (*coughs. Just once, but wrackingly, painfully*).

Rosa. That very bad cough you got, Mr. Dusty.

Dusty. It's sorta bad, Mrs. Katapouli.

Nick. You do anything for him?

Dusty. Not yet. I'll be better when I get to Albuquerque. It's warmer there, they tell me.

Rosa. Pretty cold here, all right.

Nick. Too cold to be hitch-hikin'.

Dusty. Yeah. If you hadn't of invited me in off the road I'd of prob'ly froze half to death.

Rosa. That reminds me. I better see if the cabins got plenty stovewood.

Nick. If those people in Number Nine singin' Christmas carols again, you tell 'em I said "shut up."

Rosa. All right. I tell them to sing very small.

Nick. You got folks in Albuquerque, Dusty?

Dusty. Yes. I hope so. . . . I used to have a brother. . . . I hope he's still there.

Nick. I guess he still there, maybe. But that's long ways to go by hitch-hike.

Dusty. It's pretty far. Be sorta a novelty, though. Travelin' on Christmas Eve.

Nick. I guess so, all right. (*Pause*) You like Christmas, Dusty?

Dusty. Why I dunno. Never thought about it much. I guess it's all right. Like Thanksgivin' and the Fourth of July. They're all right too, I guess. I never thought much about whether I like Christmas.

Nick. I *don't* like it. I'm prob'ly the only fella in the whole world who don't like it. (*Solemnly*) Believe me, I *hate* Christmas.

Dusty. Whatta you got against Christmas?

Nick. Plenty. Presents. And other things.

Dusty. How presents?

Nick. Well, look. People are stingy and mean most of the time . . . why not *all* the time? Why call it off on Christmas?

Dusty. I dunno. I guess it started a long time ago. When those fellas brung the gifts to the little Baby Jesus in the manger.

Nick. What fellas?

DUSTY. The fellas on the camels. You know. The wise men.

NICK. Oh. (*Pause*) What about the manger? What about that?

DUSTY. You know, the place where the little Baby was. It's a sort of a barn.

NICK. Where was the Papa and Mamma?

DUSTY. They were there too.

NICK. In the barn?

DUSTY. Um-hm.

NICK. Why didn't they go to a hotel?

DUSTY. They did. Sort of a hotel. A inn. More like a tourist camp, I guess. It was all full up. But the barn belonged to the fella that owned the inn and he took care of 'em.

NICK. He was a nice fella, hm?

DUSTY. Pretty nice, I guess. They were all tired out after such a long trip.

NICK. Where from?

DUSTY. From . . . oh yes . . . Nazareth.

NICK. Oh . . . no wonder they were tired. That's pretty far all right. (*Pause*) That *proves* what I said. Christmas was pretty good then, but it ain't any more. There ain't any nice fellas now like the one that owned that tourist camp. Everybody selfish. Me too. You bet. I don't give anybody anything. No help even.

DUSTY (*slightly amused*). Is that so?

NICK. You bet. Nope, I don't like Christmas. Ev'rybody selfish. Everywheres. Why not admit it? Anyhow, I've done away with it *here*. No Christmas at Nick's Place. Betcher life. No presents.

(*SOUND: Coffee cup in saucer.*)

NICK. Want some more coffee? Sandwiches? Pie?

DUSTY. No thanks. I gotta be on my way now. I sure appreciate the free grub, Nick. I wish I could pay you for it.

NICK. Forget it. It's only money. (*Pause*) Say! You gonna be cold!

DUSTY. Oh, I'm all right. (*He gives a slight cough.*)

NICK. I don't think so. Wait . . .

(*SOUND: Footsteps, fading, returning.*)

NICK. Here. Put on this coat.

DUSTY. But it's *yours,* Nick.

NICK. It's an old one. I don't want it any more. It don't fit me good. Anyhow I never did like it. Take it before I throw it away.

DUSTY. Gosh, Nick . . . *thanks.* . . .

NICK. Here . . . you better take some o' these here sandwiches. You'll get hungry. Here . . . ham, cheese, roast beef . . . jelly . . . stick 'em in your pocket.

DUSTY. Nick! You shouldn't do all that! You're too big-hearted for your own good!

NICK. Me? Big-hearted? (*Laughs ironically*) Ha ha! Say! I'm just as stingy as the next fella. Stingier. I just don't wanta worry 'bout you.

DUSTY. All right, Nick. And thanks. Thanks a whole lot. Well . . . I guess I'll start out.

NICK. Wait. You better stay here. Don't go. I give you a little job. We find a bed somewheres for you. Maybe I kick one o' the tourists out. You better stay.

DUSTY. Nope. Thanks just the same, Nick, but I better go. Adios. . . .

(*SOUND: Footsteps going off, downstairs.*)

NICK. So long, Dusty.

DUSTY (*calling in the distance*). G'bye, Mrs. Katapouli!

ROSA (*off*). G'bye!

(*SOUND: Footsteps climbing stairs.*)

ROSA. He go away for good?

NICK. Yes. Won't see him any more, I guess. He cough pretty bad.

ROSA. That's too bad. I'm sorry for him. (*Pause*) I'm glad you no get sick.

NICK. Me too. Knock on wood. . . .

(*SOUND: Knocking wood twice.*)

ROSA. Nick . . . I got something.

NICK. That's nice, Rosa.

ROSA. It's for you, Nick. In this little box.

NICK. What? Christmas present? *Take it back!* How many times I tell you no Christmas here? (*Pause. Defensively*) And this year I mean it.

ROSA. No! No Christmas present. I bought it for me. You can only wear it. It's a watch and chain.

NICK (*emphatically*). Don't want it. (*Interested*) Is it a *gold* watch?

ROSA. Yes. Here. I open the box.

(*SOUND: Unwrapping box.*)

ROSA. See?

NICK. Oh-h-h! Rosa! What a watch! It weigh half a pound, easy! An' gold! (*Pause*) Rosa! (*Suspiciously*) You sure this no Christmas present? You sure you buy it for *you*?

ROSA. Yes, Nick. I wear it Sundays once in a while. Maybe. Other days I lend it to you. To keep safe.

NICK. Whatta watch! What a watch an' chain!

VOICE (*calling*). Hello-o-o in there!

NICK. What's that!?

(*SOUND: Footsteps hurrying to porch.*)

ROSA. It's two people . . .

NICK. A man and a girl. (*Calls*) Come on up! Come on up the stairs!

ROSA. Look! The girl! She look very tired or something! I go help!

(*SOUND: Footsteps hurrying downstairs.*)

NICK (*to himself*). I better get busy . . . get out the easy chair for the little girl. . . .

(*SOUND: Big chair being pushed about.*)

NICK (*to himself*). Glassa water. That make her feel better.

(*SOUND: Footsteps. Running water. Footsteps.*)

NICK. There. Put it on the table. (*Pause*) Hello! Come on in. (*Pause*) Sit down. Here.

MARIA. Thank you. (*Sighs as though very tired.*)

JOSÉ. You feel better now, Maria?

MARIA. Yes, José . . . don't worry 'bout me.

NICK. You like something hot? Some coffee maybe?

MARIA. Thank you, no.

JOSÉ. I am José Santos. Maria is my wife. She very tired. We walk a long ways.

ROSA. Oh. You are very young couple.

JOSÉ. The car broke down away up the road. It's very old and no good any more . . . so we leave it and we walk and walk . . . we can't see a light anywheres. Then we see a big star over this house. The only light on the desert.

NICK. It's nice, hm?

JOSÉ. It's so beautiful. Then we walked here fast as we could. . . .

MARIA (*gives a little painful sigh*). Madre Mia . . .

JOSÉ. Maria! You all right?

MARIA. Yes, José. If . . . if I could rest a little . . . maybe?

JOSÉ. You have a cabin for us? I have money . . . a little . . .

NICK. I very sorry . . . they all full. . . .

JOSÉ. Oh-h-h. Then we must go on. Come, Maria.

ROSA. But this the only place for many miles.

NICK. Yes. It's true. There is only the desert. . . . Rosa! I know what we do. Let them take *our* room . . . yes?

ROSA. It . . . it isn't very *nice* room. . . .

JOSÉ. Oh . . . any place . . . any place at all. . . .

NICK. It's just a little shed against the house. There's the door over there. One time we keep hay in it for the cow.

ROSA. When the cabins all get filled up we have no place to sleep, so we make a little bedroom in there. Some hay is still there. But it smells good . . . the hay. Come, little one, I show you.

MARIA. But you will have no place to sleep?

NICK. We'll put sleepin' cots in here for us. We be *fine*. Maybe we wouldn't go to bed anyhow.

(*SOUND: Door opening.*)

MARIA. Oh-h! It's a *nice* room.

NICK. You put the little girl to bed, Rosa, so she rest.

(*SOUND: Door closing.*)

(*MUSIC: up, then FADE, change to cowboy music. Up, then FADE on signal to:*)

(*SOUND: Horses' hoofs, walking. Creak of leather, jingle of spurs.*)

(*MUSIC: FADE OUT.*)

BUCK. Now jest wait'll we get to the top of this here coulee and over the rise and we'll see if it's still there. . . .

CURLEY. Biggest star I *ever* see! Can't understand what it's a-doin' there . . . why it's so close to the ground like.

JOHNNY. Sure is a beautiful star. . . .

BUCK. When we get past that big boulder, we'll see if it's still there. . . .

CURLEY. Folleyed it for nigh onto three hours, covered fifteen miles, an' it's gettin' bigger all the time!

BUCK. LOOK!

(*SOUND: Sound of hoofs stops.*)

JOHNNY. There it is! Bigger'n ever! An' beautifuller!

CURLEY. An' *closer!* Almost like it was a-leadin' us on!

BUCK. Boys, I'm a-gonna see just *how* close I can get to it! *Come on!!*

(*SOUND: Horses galloping.*)

(*MUSIC: up, then fade into background music for Nick's Place, then fade out.*)

(*SOUND: Light knocking on door. Door opening.*)

NICK (*whispers hoarsely*). Is she sleepin'?

ROSA. Go 'way, Nick! This no place for you.

NICK (*whispering*). But Rosa, I wanta tell you . . . that boy . . . Dusty . . . he's been out in the road tryin' to catch a ride, all this time!

ROSA. Oh! Nearly three hours he's been out there an' it's cold! Bring 'im in, then! Right away!

(*SOUND: Door closes. Footsteps.*)

NICK (*calling*). Dusty! . . . DUSTY!

DUSTY (*off*). Hello-o-o-o!

NICK. Come inside! Right away! You get sick standing out there all night! Come in!

(*SOUND: Footsteps running up stairs.*)

DUSTY. Br-r-r-r! It's cold out there. (*Laughs*) I guess those people don't like me, Nick. The ones in the big cars.

NICK. That proves what I say! The Christmas spirit! Haha! They let you wear your thumb out! Come here an' drink some hot coffee an' eat something, quick!

(*SOUND: Stool pushed back, pouring coffee, rattle of plates.*)

NICK. You stay right here with Rosa and me till you get better or it gets warmer or something.

(*SOUND: Door opens, closes.*)

ROSA (*loud whisper*). Nick! Nick!

NICK. Whattsa matter, Rosa?

ROSA (*loud whisper*). That Doctor! . . . the old man . . . where is he?

NICK. Number Seven Cabin. The girl . . . she get sick?

ROSA. Pretty sick! . . . I get the Doctor!

NICK. Wait! *I* get him! Let *me!*

ROSA. No! . . . no, I can tell him better. . . .

(*SOUND: Hurrying footsteps downstairs.*)

DUSTY. What's up?

NICK. A young fella and his wife. She pretty sick, I guess. I thought she just tired.

DUSTY. Oh . . . that's too bad.

NICK. Yeah. . . . Say . . . Dusty . . .

DUSTY. Hm?

NICK. How the Papa and Mama get to that town . . . you know. . . .

DUSTY. What town? Oh . . . Bethlehem. Well . . . I saw a picture of it once . . . they had a little donkey.

NICK. Oh. That ain't much, is it? Dusty, you got a map? Of the world?

DUSTY. Why, no. What would I be doing with that, Nick? Say, wait. I got a little pocket-notebook with all sorts of little maps in it. Here. They're awful small, though. Why?

NICK. Where's that other town . . . Naza . . . whatta you call it?

DUSTY. Nazareth?

NICK. That's the one. Where is it?

DUSTY. Let's see . . . well, I always understood it was in Jerusalem. Yeah, that's where it is all right. Must be.

NICK. Oh.

(*SOUND: Hurried footsteps upstairs.*)

Dusty. Mrs. Katapouli is back already with the Doctor.

Rosa. Hurry, Doctor! She is in this little room over here!

(*SOUND: Door opens.*)

Rosa. Doctor, this is the husband.

Doctor. My boy, you'd better go out and talk to Nick and Dusty for a while.

José. All right.

(*SOUND: Door closing.*)

Nick. Hello, José. You better have something to eat. Sit down. (*Kindly*) Don't be so worried.

(*SOUND: Clatter of dishes, pouring coffee.*)

Nick. Dusty, this is José.

Dusty. Glad to know you. Shake!

José. Hello.

Nick. Drink the coffee. You'll feel better. . . .

(*SOUND: spoon in cup.*)

Nick. Dusty, where's the map?

Dusty. Right here.

Nick. Now. Where is this Jerusalem?

Dusty. Why, I think it's over by that green place somewheres . . . or around by Africa . . . there it is.

Nick. Oh. (*Sighs with relief*) So that's it. Now . . . where's Bethelehem?

(*SOUND: Coffee cup hitting saucer with a clatter.*)

José. Where is what did you say?

Dusty. Bethlehem. You know where it is?

José. Yes. Sure I know. We're going there, Maria and I. We were.

Nick. Honest?

Dusty. You're fooling.

José. Oh, no, there is no reason I should fool you. That's where my people live. I was taking Maria there so's she'd be safe

... because I have no work and just a little money. Of course. Bethlehem. I used to live there with my people. Bethlehem. Pennsylvania.

NICK. Is that *right? Pennsylvania?*

JOSÉ. I'm sure of it.

NICK. That's a terrible far ways from Nazareth ... even on this little map ... it say ... "One quarter inch equal five hundred miles." ... (*Awed*) And it's *three inches, easy.* (*He is staggered.*)

DUSTY (*gently*). Maybe we got it mixed up somewheres.

(*SOUND: Boots tramping on the porch.*)

BUCK. Howdy!

NICK (*still stunned by the distance from Nazareth to Bethlehem, Pa.*). Hello. Come on in.

DUSTY. Hi.

BUCK. That's *some* star you got out there, friend.

NICK. You like it?

BUCK. It's a beauty.

NICK (*cordially*). Come on in!

BUCK. Wait'll I get my pardners. They're standin' around down there lookin' up at your star. (*Calls*) Come on up, fellas. It's a rest'rant or sump'n.

NICK. Tourist camp.

VOICE (*off*). Comin' up!

BUCK. We been on a trip to town. Sorta a vacation for one day. Ridin' back to the ranch now.

NICK. Oh. Well, have some coffee an' sandwiches an' pie.

BUCK. Don't mind if I do.

(*SOUND: Boots climbing stairs.*)

JOHNNY (*off on porch, whistles*). Phew-w-w! Look at that there star!

CURLEY. Lights up half the county!

NICK. Come right in, boys.

JOHNNY. Thanks.

BUCK. We was ridin' along out on the desert when we see that there big star. . . .

CURLEY. Folleyed it for eighteen mile.

JOHNNY. Maybe more'n that, even.

(*SOUND: Door opening. Very faintly is heard sound of new-born baby crying. Door closes.*)

NICK. What's that?

DUSTY. It sounded like a . . . naw, it *couldn't* be. . . .

ROSA. Nick! It's a little baby! A little boy!

DUSTY. Well! Congratulations, José!

JOSÉ. I . . . I . . . what did you say . . . a *boy!* . . . oh! I must see my Maria!

(*SOUND: Hurrying footsteps. Door opening.*)

JOSÉ. Doctor! Doctor! . . . Can I go in? . . . Can I see my Maria . . . *please!*

DOCTOR. Why, of course, my boy! You can see both of them. . . . Mother and child.

JOSÉ. Oh! . . . Thank you! (*Pause*) . . . oh . . . Maria! . . .

(*SOUND: Sound of door closing.*)

BUCK. A *baby*. . . .

CURLEY. A boy baby!

ROSA. Nick . . . the mother . . . she say she want you to be godfather. . . .

NICK. Ain't it wonderful? My place, too! Doctor! Come and have something to eat! You too, Rosa! Celebrate! Everybody eat! Look! I have surprise!

(*SOUND: Clatter of dishes.*)

NICK. Cold turkey! Wine! Cake! Pie! Cramberry sauce! The whole works! I was savin' it for the tourists for dinner to-morrow. But *we* need it!

ROSA. Go 'way, Nick. I fix.

JOHNNY. Hey! Buck! I was just thinkin'!

BUCK. What about?

JOHNNY. All that stuff we bought in town! . . .

BUCK. What stuff? Oh . . . the presents?

NICK (*suspiciously*). Presents? *What* presents?

CURLEY. When we were in town we bought a whole lot o' things.

BUCK. None of us got anybody to give presents to . . . and it was Christmas . . . so we went around to a store and bought a lot of presents anyway.

JOHNNY. We were gonna look for somebody to give 'em to . . . then we saw the big star and sorta forgot about it.

BUCK. Say . . . do you think . . . that is . . . maybe *he'd* like to have 'em, Ma'am. The baby, I mean.

ROSA. I think so all right.

CURLEY. He's the only one we got to give 'em to. . . .

JOHNNY. We'd like a powerful lot for him to have 'em. . . . Here, Ma'am. Look! Hold out your hands . . . we'll fill 'em up with presents. . . .

(*SOUND: Jingle of little ornaments, jewelry.*)

JOHNNY. See? . . . rings . . . a little gold box . . . doo-dads . . . a whole lot o' things. . . . I bought ev'rything looked like gold. . . . I like gold things. . . .

CURLEY. Here's mine . . . it's some stuff that smells nice . . . the lady that sold it to me said you put a match to it and the smoke smells good. . . .

ROSA. Oh . . . incense . . . that's nice. . . .

BUCK. I got some pretty colored soap and nice-smellin' stuff you sprinkle on your clothes to make 'em smell sweet and a lot of other things . . . here . . . take 'em. . . .

121

ROSA. Oh-h-h . . . they're all *beautiful*. . . . I . . . I'll take them to him right away and put them on his pillow.

CURLEY. Tell him we're sorry they ain't wrapped up purty. We forgot that part.

ROSA. Oh, they're much prettier this way . . . such nice baby presents. . . . I go in now and give them to him.

NICK. Rosa! Wait! I . . . I have something for you, too. A sort of a necklace. . . . (*Pause*.)

ROSA. Oh, Nick!

NICK (*sternly*). No Christmas present, though. I bought it for me. But you can wear it a while, Rosa.

ROSA. I like it! I like it, Nick! I like *you!* (*Sound of loud kisses from* ROSA.)

NICK. Rosa! Stop kissing me! We're married people!

ROSA. Oh, I'm so glad I marry you! You a kind man!

NICK. Rosa! Please! Stop!

ROSA. One day in Elkhorn a horse fall down in the street and hurt his leg. And I see a man cry because he so sorry for the horse. And I ask, "What is that man's name?" And they say, "Nick Katapouli." So I go home and write "Rosa Katapouli" on a paper. And I like it. So I marry him.

NICK. Me kind? I should say not! (*Proudly*) Rosa, I am a cruel man.

ROSA. Sure! I know. (*Laughs*) I go in and give the pretty things to the baby now. . . .

(*SOUND: Door gently opens, closes*.)

BUCK. I hope he likes our presents. . . .

CURLEY (*softly*). I shore hope so. . . .

(*MUSIC: From a distance voices are heard, singing far away, softly, "Silent Night, Holy Night."* . . .)

DUSTY. That's a wonderful star, Nick.

NICK. Nice, hm?

DUSTY. Turn the lights out in here and it shows up even better.

(*SOUND: Lights switched off.*)

(*MUSIC: Singing up a little.*)

DUSTY. Nick . . . those people in Number Nine are singin' Christmas carols again . . . you gonna tell 'em to shut up?

NICK. Hm? . . . oh . . . well, not yet. . . . (*Pause*) Maybe after while . . . (*Pause*) . . . oh . . . let 'em sing. . . .

(*MUSIC: As if in answer the voices come up louder.*)

NICK. I think . . . I think I go out an' look at my star. . . .

(*MUSIC: Voices up full, fade as music begins. Music up full, then fade.*)

NARRATOR. The title, *The Desert Shall Rejoice,* is taken from the book of Isaiah, the thirty-fifth chapter. "The wilderness and the solitary place shall be glad for them, and the desert shall rejoice, and blossom as the rose."

(*MUSIC: Up, "Joy To The World."*)

OUR LOVE

A Radio Romance

By

PALMER THOMPSON

CAST

JOHN SMITH, *An American Selectee*
MARY SMITH, *His wife*

OUR LOVE

ANNOUNCER. And now to our story for tonight. . . . Not a
great story . . . but a small story . . . of two little people
. . . two small lives . . . because Manhattan, big as it is, is
made up of little things. Little people, little houses, little apartments, and it's in one of those apartments that our story starts.
Two rooms and a kitchenette, crowded with men, reporters,
not noisy, turbulent, shouting . . . but quietly respectful,
standing with hat in hand . . . listening to a young woman
and her story.

(*MUSIC: In low with a melancholy undertone, hold then fade
down and under and out.*)

MARY (*quietly, calmly, with a sad smile in her voice*). I'm afraid
you're wasting your time, gentlemen. There's nothing to
write about us . . . we're just ordinary people . . . and ordinary people aren't in the papers . . . they read them. What?
Unusual? No . . . no . . . I can't think of anything unusual
John ever did . . . unless . . . well no. . . . I guess a lot of
people met the way we did. How? Well, you might have
called it a pick-up meeting. It was at a concert at Lewisohn
Stadium some years ago . . . in the summer. It was awfully
hot that day and while I'm not really a music lover . . . it
was nice and cool sitting there in the evening and hearing the
music come to you from a distance. They had just played the
last number, something by Tschaikowsky . . . I don't know
the real name but they call it . . . *Our Love*. Anyway I sat

there as most of the crowd filed out catching as much of the coolness as I could . . . when I noticed a man just a little way off . . . staring at me . . . I was annoyed so I turned my back to him . . . the next thing I knew . . . he was beside me.

(*MUSIC: In, hold, then slow fade.*)

JOHN. Pardon me, Miss . . .

MARY. What!

JOHN. Please, . . . please don't think I'm fresh . . . but I like you.

MARY. Well . . . I never . . .

JOHN. I know it sounds crazy . . . but I'm not really, . . . it's just . . . just that I'm lonely, I guess.

MARY. The very idea . . . going around talking to people like that. . . .

JOHN. I'm sorry, Miss.

MARY. I certainly hope I don't look like someone you can just pick up.

JOHN. No, . . . you don't. . . . I suppose that's why I talked to you.

MARY. You might just as well have saved your breath.

JOHN. But I didn't so I guess I'll just have to apologize and go.

MARY. No . . . wait . . . why . . . why did you pick me out to talk to?

JOHN. Just a feeling I had . . . A feeling that I'd like you . . . like to talk to you.

MARY. Feeling?

JOHN. Yes. . . . I don't know if this ever happened to you . . . but did you ever go into a subway, you sit down, you look across the aisle and all of a sudden you see someone . . . a man or a woman . . . and for no reason at all . . . you never saw them before . . . you'll never see them again . . . you

128

dislike them intensely . . . so intensely that you want to get up and slap them in the face . . . but you don't, 'cause you're civilized.

MARY. And that's the way you felt about me?

JOHN. Yes . . . only I like you . . . and for once I wasn't civilized.

MARY. I'm glad everybody doesn't act like you.

JOHN. I don't know . . . New York might be a better town to live in if they did.

MARY. What do you mean?

JOHN. Well, if I saw you in my town . . . the place that I come from . . . I'd eventually have met someone you knew . . . and we'd have been properly introduced.

MARY. But not in New York.

JOHN. No . . . it's pretty hard to meet one person in seven million . . . when you don't know any of the others.

MARY. Well, now you've met me . . . I hope you're satisfied.

JOHN. I would be completely . . . if you'd have a soda or something with me.

MARY (*wavering*). Well . . .

JOHN. Please . . . what can you lose?

MARY. I shouldn't. . . .

JOHN. But you will. . . .

MARY. Well, a free soda is a free soda . . . all right.

(*MUSIC: In, hold, then fade down and under.*)

MARY. And that was the way I met John. . . . I suppose when you look back on it, it doesn't seem proper . . . but at the time . . . it was the most natural thing in the world. . . . Johnny liked me and talked to me . . . I liked him and talked to him. What? When did he propose? Oh, not for a long while afterwards. Love at first sight? I don't think that happens . . . except perhaps in the movies. You see, I went

with Johnny two years before we were married . . . and the
first year it was just fun . . . we liked each other, laughed
at the same things . . . enjoyed the same pictures . . . and
that was important . . . we learned to like each other before
we thought of love . . . then we knew it was serious when I
started paying my own way . . . buying my own tickets to
the movies . . . picking up my half of the check in the cafe-
terias we ate at. You see, Johnny only made twenty-two dollars a week . . . and you can't have fun for two people on
that and save much out of it. How did he propose? Let me
see . . . come to think of it . . . I don't remember that
Johnny ever really did propose . . . no . . . wait a minute
. . . that's right he did . . . I made him. That sounds brazen,
doesn't it . . . but it's not really. It happened on another one
of those warm city evenings . . . we were economizing, so
instead of spending twenty-five cents to go into a movie and
cool off . . . we spent five cents for a ferry ride to Staten
Island.

(*MUSIC: In, hold, then fade down and out.*)

(*SOUND: Ferry boat and waves lapping against its side as it
plows through the water. Then off mike in the background
we hear an old accordion playing some Italian song.*)

JOHN. Gosh . . . it's nice here. . . . I'm glad we did this instead
of going to a movie . . . it was a swell idea.

MARY. I've got a lot of swell ideas.

JOHN. Where'd you get them from?

MARY. My old boy friends.

JOHN. Go on . . . you never had an old boy friend.

MARY. Aren't you the conceited one. . . .

JOHN. Oh . . . gee . . . I knew there was something I forgot.

MARY. What?

JOHN. I love you.

OUR LOVE

MARY. Thank you, kind sir . . . now what do I do . . . curtsy?

JOHN. You might . . . after all I don't love everyone.

MARY. I hope not . . . what's the name of that song he's playing, Johnny?

JOHN. I don't know . . . it sounds Italian. . . .

MARY. It's kinda romantic.

JOHN. Uh . . . oh . . . I guess maybe we shoulda gone to the movies.

MARY. Why do you say that?

JOHN. Well, if it's romance you want . . . Charles Boyer is a lot better at it than I am.

MARY. Yes . . . but he's not as close.

JOHN. I guess that's my cue to snuggle up. Wait a minute. (*Calling*) Hey! Hey you! Do you know the song . . . *Our Love*. Yeah? Here's a dime . . . play it.

(SOUND: *Off mike clink of a coin on the deck then in the distance the accordion picks up . . . "Our Love."*)

MARY. Johnny . . . you shouldn't have. That was ten cents.

JOHN. I know . . . but we've saved enough money for one evening . . . it won't break us. There. How's this?

MARY. Nice.

JOHN. Close enough?

MARY. Yes.

JOHN. You don't know how lucky you are . . . music by Tschaikowsky . . . light by the moon . . . and arms by Johnny Smith.

MARY. I like the last best.

JOHN. So do I. (*Pause*) What are you thinking of?

MARY. Us.

JOHN. What about us?

MARY. I don't know . . . just us.

JOHN. Dreaming?

MARY. Yes . . . you too?

JOHN. Sure.

MARY. About what?

JOHN. Oh . . . minks and sable and yachts and penthouses.

MARY. Johnny . . . don't be silly.

JOHN. And how I'm not going to give you any of them.

MARY. Well, I like that. . . .

JOHN. I guess maybe I'm not ambitious enough.

MARY. Meaning what?

JOHN. All I want to give you is a house and me . . . a steady job
. . . some security . . . but mostly me.

MARY. Isn't that a coincidence. . . .

JOHN. Why?

MARY. That's just what I want.

JOHN. And you're going to have it.

MARY. When, Johnny?

JOHN. What?

MARY. I said when, Johnny.

JOHN. I don't know . . . soon I hope . . . but it doesn't look
like it.

MARY. Why not now?

JOHN. Now?

MARY. Yes.

JOHN. I only wish it could be, hon . . . but I'm making twenty-
two bucks a week . . . we couldn't live on that.

MARY. And I'm making eighteen.

JOHN. Oh!

MARY. Eighteen and twenty-two is forty dollars—that's a nice
income.

JOHN. Yeah, . . . yeah, it is at that . . . but you'd have to work
then.

MARY. What difference would that make?

JOHN. Well, coming home and doing the housework and everything.

MARY. You'd do your share of it. . . . I'd see to that.

JOHN. Of course I would . . . but it would be awfully hard, Mary.

MARY. If the hardship scares us . . . we may as well not get married.

JOHN. I didn't mean for me, dear . . . I meant for you.

MARY. And I meant for both of us . . . after all if we can't stick together through hard times . . . it's better to find it out sooner . . . than later.

JOHN. Maybe you're right, honey . . . who knows when I'll get a better job . . . it might be years . . . yeah, the more I think of it, the better it sounds.

MARY. There's only one thing.

JOHN. What?

MARY. You've never asked me to marry you.

JOHN. Is that all? You scared me for a minute.

MARY. All . . . isn't that enough?

JOHN. You know how I feel about you, Mary, a guy doesn't have to say those things.

MARY. But a girl likes to hear them.

JOHN. I can't propose . . . I'd feel silly.

MARY. Johnny Smith . . . you're going to propose to me.

JOHN. Gee, Mary. . . .

MARY. I can't have a big wedding or any of those things but one thing I want to remember is you and . . .

JOHN. All right, hon . . . how do you want it . . . with a French accent . . . à la Boyer.

MARY. I'm not fooling, Johnny.

JOHN. And neither am I, Mary; I never really thought about

how I'd say this. I always sort of figured that since we've gone together so long . . . well, you know what I mean . . . I've got the words but they're locked up in my heart and I can't seem to get them out . . . all I can say, Mary, is simply . . . I love you . . . will you marry me?

MARY (*simply*). Yes, Johnny.

(*MUSIC: In, hold, then fade down and under.*)

MARY. Two weeks later John and I were married. It wasn't much of a wedding . . . we took a day off from work and went down to the City Hall. . . . John paid two dollars for the license . . . and I paid two dollars for the marriage certificate . . . because that was the way it was going to be . . . fifty-fifty from the start. . . . I remember Johnny almost laughed at our wedding and it was funny. The city clerk was a big fat man . . . he looked just like those cartoons you have in the papers of politicians . . . and his face was red and his nose was redder . . . not from sunburn I'm afraid . . . but, funny or not, there it was . . . our wedding. Mr. John Smith and Miss Mary Alden beame Mr. and Mrs. John Smith. What? No . . . no we didn't get the house . . . there wasn't enough money for that . . . instead we took this apartment . . . it was cheap . . . only thirty-five dollars a month and a lot easier to furnish. We went down to an installment house, just paid ten dollars down and told them where we worked and we got all the furniture. Of course there were a lot of debts but we managed to pay them off in the first year . . . that was the year the draft law was passed. Going into the second year everything was going to be . . . as Johnny would have said . . . peaches and cream. We figured on putting a little money in the bank toward the down payment of that house . . . and maybe . . . but that's not

important. Anyway one day in October, 1940 I came home.
Johnny was there ahead of me.

(*MUSIC: In, hold, then down and out.*)

(*SOUND: Door closing.*)

MARY (*slightly off mike*). You home, Johnny?

JOHN. Yes . . . hon . . . in the parlor.

MARY. Been home long?

JOHN. About two hours.

MARY. Two hours! Then supper should be . . . (*Surprised*)
Two hours! Johnny, what's wrong? You haven't been fired?

JOHN. No, honey . . . take it easy . . . I haven't been fired.

MARY. But coming home in the middle of the afternoon . . .
what happened?

JOHN. Nothing, Mary . . . just sit down and I'll explain.

MARY. Don't tell me your boss got big hearted and gave you
the afternoon off.

JOHN. Hardly . . . if there's anything big about my boss, it's
not his heart.

MARY. You're sure you haven't been fired? Don't be afraid to
tell me, darling.

JOHN. No, I haven't been fired . . . that is, not exactly.

MARY. Not exactly.

JOHN. Well, here it is all at once . . . I've been down to see about
enlisting in the Army.

MARY. Enlisting? I don't understand. Why?

JOHN. Well, I figure with this draft coming on, maybe it'll be
better if I get the jump on them.

MARY. But that's silly, John . . . they won't draft you . . .
you're married . . . they'll defer you.

JOHN. For how long?

MARY. What difference does that make?

JOHN. A lot maybe. . . . Look at it this way. Right now my job isn't any too good and if I lose it, well, it doesn't make much difference.

MARY. I don't see . . .

JOHN. But suppose a couple of years from now I've got a good job . . . a job that I like and make money at . . . then my number in the draft will come up and I'll have to go . . . and that wouldn't be so hot.

MARY. But it's so foolish . . . this'll be all over soon . . . and they probably won't even call the married men.

JOHN. I hope you're right, hon . . . but even so the law's for five years and they'll surely get around to me in that time.

MARY. Maybe . . . but why don't you wait until they do. . . .

JOHN. Because we couldn't make any plans, darling. You know me. . . . I'm no rah, rah, boy . . . hooray for the red, white and blue . . . but I'm telling you what I think is the wise thing to do.

MARY. Wise?

JOHN. Sure . . . this way I'll get my year in . . . and when I get out . . . well, we should be able to save a little money so that I can look around for a really good job.

MARY. But a whole year, Johnny.

JOHN. And if I don't get one . . . I can always get my old job back.

MARY. It's such a long time.

JOHN. It won't be so bad . . . we can write to each other . . . I'll get leaves . . . who knows, . . . maybe I'll even be stationed right around here.

MARY. You haven't enlisted already, Johnny?

JOHN. Of course not . . . you know I wouldn't do a thing like that without talking it over with you first.

MARY. It'd be the first time we've been separated since we were married.

JOHN. It's just a year, honey . . . that's not so long. We've got a lot more than that ahead of us, I hope.

MARY. Do you think this is the right thing to do, Johnny?

JOHN. Yes, I do, Mary . . . besides look at the bright side of it.

MARY. The bright side?

JOHN. Sure . . . statistics prove that forty percent of divorces occur in the second year of marriage. Well, we'll just skip the second year and eliminate forty percent of our chances of getting divorced.

MARY. I'd take that chance, Johnny.

JOHN. So would I . . . I'm just kidding, I wanted to . . .

MARY. I know . . . put the sugar coating on.

JOHN. Well . . . what do you say, Mary. I know it won't be easy . . . especially for you.

MARY. Oh, I'll get along all right . . . I always have . . . it's just . . .

JOHN. I know . . . the separation . . . that's the hardest part . . . too bad the Army doesn't make allowances for wives.

MARY. So I guess the wife will have to make allowances for the Army.

JOHN. Then you agree with me?

MARY. If you think it's the right thing to do, Johnny, then you do it . . . and remember I'm always with you in whatever you do . . . no matter what.

(*MUSIC: In, hold, then down and out.*)

MARY. So there it was . . . Johnny in the Army . . . me in New York. They sent him down South and for six whole months I didn't see him . . . but it wasn't as bad as it sounds . . . there were the letters. Every single day a letter

from Johnny and every single day I wrote one to him. What?
Yes . . . every day. What did we write about? Oh . . . silly
things mostly . . . I've still got them . . . Johnny's letters.
I remember when he came home on leave we read some of
them over . . . and laughed at them. I'd write about the new
dress I bought, the movie I saw, and how much I loved him.
He'd write about the places he'd been, the officers he had
and how much he loved me. We laughed over the parts about
love . . . it's funny how silly love sounds on paper . . .
when it's not really. Then . . . at the end of six months . . .
Johnny came home. . . . I got his letter telling me that he
would just have two days before his leave started. I guess I
was the most excited person in New York. Johnny didn't
want me to meet him at the station . . . he thought we'd miss
each other . . . but I couldn't wait. I sent him a telegram saying I'd be waiting for him at the Thirty-sixth Street and Eighth
Avenue corner of the Pennsylvania Station. Johnny's train was
due at seven in the morning . . . I got there at six . . . the
train got there at nine . . . I've never been more nervous in
my life. . . . I walked, waited in turn . . . I looked at the
clock . . . it was just going on nine . . . when I felt a hand
grasp my arm. . . .

(*MUSIC: In, hold, then fade down and out.*)

(*SOUND: Street noises in the background.*)

JOHN. Hello, hon.

MARY. Johnny.

JOHN. Yeah . . . it's me. No. Not here, Mary . . . I don't like
mushing on the street. Save it for later.

MARY. Johnny . . . it's . . . Johnny.

JOHN. I know . . . me too.

MARY. Well . . . come on . . . let's go.

JOHN. Where?

OUR LOVE

MARY. Home. Joan's sharing the apartment with me . . . but she's going to stay with her mother this week.

JOHN. Oh no . . . let her keep it . . . no apartment for us this week.

MARY. But . . .

JOHN. We'll go to a hotel . . . some swell place.

MARY. Swell?

JOHN. Well, maybe not so swell . . . but a place where you can have breakfast in bed . . . and all kinds of service . . . nothing but the best.

MARY. But the money, Johnny . . . we can't afford . . .

JOHN. Look, hon . . . I've got sixty bucks in my pocket and seven days with you . . . and for once we're not going to think about money.

MARY. All right, Johnny . . . whatever you say . . . but where did you get all that money?

JOHN. Saved it here and there . . . picked up a little playing cards . . . but that's not important . . . the important thing is we're together again. Ouch! Hey, don't squeeze my arm so hard.

MARY. I just want to make sure you don't escape.

JOHN. As if I'd try to . . . well, let's start looking for that hotel.

(MUSIC: In, hold, then fade down and out.)

JOHN. How do you like it, hon?

MARY. It's lovely . . . but doesn't it cost too . . .

JOHN. If you say that once more, Mary . . . I'll . . . I'll . . .

MARY. Consider it unsaid, Johnny.

JOHN. That's better.

MARY. And now I've got a surprise for you.

JOHN. What?

MARY. I've been saving up a sort of furlough fund myself so here's thirty dollars more . . . it's not as much . . .

JOHN. Keep it, hon . . . you may need it after I go back.

MARY. I will not . . . if you can be crazy with sixty dollars . . . I can be half as crazy with thirty dollars. We'll just make this that honeymoon we never had.

JOHN. Okay . . . why not. Now where do we go from here?

MARY. It's your leave, darling . . . whatever you say.

JOHN. Oh . . . the movies, maybe a play . . . and afterwards dinner in some classy restaurant.

(*MUSIC: In, hold, then fade down and out.*)

(*SOUND: Dinner music in the background with the sedate clatter of dishes à la Longchamps.*)

JOHN. This is really something . . . table service dishes. I'd like to see that mess sergeant of mine now.

MARY. Wasn't the food any good down there?

JOHN. Oh no . . . it was swell . . . but heavy stuff, man stuff . . . right now I'm in the mood for something fency-shmency.

MARY. What are you going to have?

JOHN. I don't know . . . let's see . . . ah, here it is . . . crêpes suzettes. . . . I've always wanted to taste that.

MARY. You won't like it, Johnny.

JOHN. Sure I will . . . you don't know me . . . I'm one of the idle rich this week.

MARY. All right . . . but don't say I didn't warn you.

JOHN. Nothing doing . . . crêpes suzettes I want . . . and crêpes suzettes it is.

(*MUSIC: In, hold, then fade down and out.*)

JOHN (*disgusted*). All right, hon . . . you can say it now.

MARY. What?

JOHN. I told you so. Crêpes suzettes! Wine and pancakes . . . phooey. . . . I'd rather have a hot dog and sauerkraut any day . . . say there's an idea . . . let's go down to the Island tomorrow.

MARY. Coney Island?

JOHN. Yeah . . . what do you say?

MARY. If you want it . . . Coney Island it is.

(*MUSIC: In, hold, then fade down and out.*)

(*SOUND: Background noises of Coney Island. Hold under the entire scene bringing the noise up when indicated.*)

MARY. I will not, Johnny Smith . . . that's one thing I will **not** go on.

JOHN. Aw, come on, Mary . . . it's not dangerous.

MARY. I can't stand roller coasters . . . you know that.

JOHN. But this is different, Mary. It's a bob sled . . . we get a whole car to ourselves . . . and sit down on the floor. . . . I'll have my arms around you all the time.

MARY. But it goes up and down so fast.

JOHN. Aw, come on, Mary . . . what do you say?

MARY. You win again, I suppose . . . let's go.

(*SOUND: Background noise up with the roar of a roller coaster, shrieking voices, shrill screams, then lots of laughter, and more noise. Then bring it down and hold in back.*)

MARY. I'll never do that any more, Johnny . . . I still haven't got my breath back.

JOHN. Go on . . . you enjoyed it . . . you were laughing all the time.

MARY. Screaming, you mean . . . oooh . . . frozen custard, Johnny . . . let's have one.

JOHN. Okay.

(*SOUND: Shooting gallery in the background.*)

JOHN. What flavor?

MARY. Vanilla.

JOHN. Two custards, buddy . . . one chocolate, one vanilla . . . yeah . . . in the cones. Thanks . . . here you are.

(*SOUND: Cash register rings off mike.*)

JOHN. Good, honey?

MARY. Wonderful . . . what'll we do now?

JOHN. I want to try my luck at the shooting gallery. . . .

MARY. Why waste money, Johnny . . . you never could hit anything.

JOHN. Ah . . . that was before . . . wait'll you see what six months in the Army did for me. Here . . . hold my cone. Hey . . . feller, let's have a gun. Now . . . watch this, Mary.

(*SOUND: Five sharp rifle shots.*)

MARY. Johnny . . . you're marvelous.

JOHN. That was nothing . . . get this. . . .

(*SOUND: Five more shots.*)

JOHN. Not bad, eh, hon?

MARY. I should say not.

JOHN. Wait . . . I'll try another load . . .

MARY. Not now, Johnny . . . your custard's melting.

JOHN. Okay . . . later then . . . enjoying yourself?

MARY. It's wonderful, Johnny. . . . I only wish it could last forever . . . that time would stop right here and now.

(*MUSIC: In, holds, then fades down and out.*)

JOHN. Train leaves in an hour, hon.

MARY. I know.

JOHN. Gosh . . . don't look so sad . . .we had fun . . . didn't we, darling?

MARY. Of course we did.

JOHN. Besides, I'll be back in six months . . . out of the Army forever . . . then we'll be together always.

MARY. But what about . . . (*Stops.*)

JOHN. What about what?

OUR LOVE

MARY. Nothing.

JOHN. Come on, Mary . . . you've got something on your mind . . . tell me.

MARY. The draft law, Johnny, it's been extended to more than a year . . . you know that.

JOHN. Is that all you're worried about. . . .

MARY. I didn't want to mention it before. . . .

JOHN. Well, you should have, hon . . . and gotten it off your mind . . . because that doesn't apply to me.

MARY. It doesn't?

JOHN. No. I asked my C.O. about it. Married men will get out after one year . . . by just asking for a discharge . . . and I'm married . . . I hope.

MARY. Really, Johnny?

JOHN. Sure . . . now perk that chin up and we'll say goodbye.

MARY. I'll come down to the station with you.

JOHN. No . . . I don't want you to, Mary. There'll be a big crowd there . . . half of them laughing, half of them crying . . . you can't say goodbyes . . . like that.

MARY. All right, Johnny.

JOHN. So this is it . . . but I'll be back in six months . . . just keep remembering that.

MARY. I will.

JOHN. Oh . . . I knew there was something I forgot.

MARY. What?

JOHN (*flippant*). I love you, hon.

MARY (*simply*). Me too, Johnny.

(*MUSIC: In, holds, then fades down and out.*)

MARY. So Johnny's leave was over . . . but the memory of it wasn't . . . we relived it a thousand times and more in our letters to each other . . . it's funny how the past can bring so

143

much happiness to the present. What? Yes, I saw him again. It happened just as he said it would . . . they released him at the end of the year . . . and he came home and we resumed our ordinary lives. Johnny got another job . . . a different one . . . it didn't pay much more than the old one . . . but the important thing was he liked his work. I kept on with my position because twenty-eight dollars a week still isn't enough for two people to live on. We figured that after a year or so we'd have saved up enough, what with Johnny's raises, for me to quit my job. Then we could really start having a home and all that goes with it. Things went along smoothly . . . the movies on Saturday night . . . the papers on Sunday morning . . . until *that* Sunday morning. Johnny had turned on the radio . . . and we weren't really listening to it . . . when the news flash came over. He looked at me . . . I didn't say anything. Then he stepped over to the radio and switched it off.

(*MUSIC: In, hold, then fade down and out.*)

JOHN. That's it, hon.

MARY. But it can't be true, Johnny, out of a clear sky . . .

JOHN. It can and it is . . . maybe the skies weren't as clear as we thought . . . maybe we've been blinding ourselves.

MARY. This means you'll have to go back?

JOHN. Of course it does.

MARY. But not right away, Johnny . . . you can wait until they call you.

JOHN. What's the sense in that?

MARY. We'll be together.

JOHN. Yeah . . . sitting here . . . waiting for the letter, the ax to fall. Don't you see, honey . . . it's no good . . . we've been waiting too long. . . . I guess that's the trouble . . . maybe we deserved this.

144

OUR LOVE

MARY. Not us, Johnny . . . we never hurt anyone . . . we're just little people . . . we never bothered.

JOHN. No, we never bothered . . . that's the whole key . . . our whole lives were wrapped up in ourselves . . . four walls and an apartment . . . that was our world . . . then somebody comes along and slaps us in the face and we wake up. . . . I only hope it's not too late.

MARY. I don't care. Johnny . . . I don't care what the radio said . . . about Pearl Harbor or anything . . . I don't want you to go. Stay with me . . . wait until they call you.

JOHN. What for . . . what . . .

MARY. We're married.

JOHN. That's not being married, sitting together clinging . . . holding each other. . . . I don't want that and you don't either. People don't get married just to be together.

MARY. But we're in love, Johnny.

JOHN. Sure . . . but marriage is a lot more than love . . . it's making plans . . . dreaming of the home you're going to have in the future . . . putting aside a little for that vacation . . . having kids . . . but most of all making plans . . . together . . . two people . . . and we can't do that now . . . not as long as . . . this goes on . . . don't you see, honey . . . my way . . . it's the only way . . . I've got to go back now . . . get it over with . . . and maybe if I go back soon enough . . . I'll come back sooner.

MARY. But, Johnny, maybe . . .

JOHN. Yeah . . . I know what you're thinking . . . me too . . . but we'll have to take that chance . . . anyway it's better than living with no future . . . honey . . . this is the hardest thing we ever had to do . . . but it's the only thing we can do . . . you see that . . . don't you?

MARY. Yes, Johnny . . . I see it.

OUR LOVE

(*MUSIC: In, hold, then fade down and out.*)

MARY. That was the way it happened. Johnny went back in khaki . . . and I . . . I went back to living with letters again. Yes . . . he still wrote . . . every day. Only this time the letters were more serious . . . there was nothing to laugh at in them. Then came his last letter . . . oh, there were postcards after that . . . but I mean his last long letter . . . when I read it . . . I could just hear him talking to me . . . saying the words.

(*MUSIC: In, hold, then down and under.*)

JOHN. Dear Mary . . . this may be the last letter you get from me for some time. . . . Our outfit's packing up and getting ready to move out. I don't know where we're going and even if I did I couldn't tell you. The censor would cut it out. Anyway you can still write letters to me . . . send them to this address and I'll still get them. Another thing you can send is cigarettes . . . they may be scarce where we're going. Since they've increased my pay, I've increased my allotment to you. I know none of this is new, but it's kind of hard to write things when you know somebody else is going to read this letter. Anyway, honey, I don't want you to worry about me, and just remember that I love you. There's a lot of other things I'd like to say, but I never was good at words. I'll leave them unsaid the way they've always been between us and close with all my love. John.

(*MUSIC: Up, hold, then down and out.*)

MARY. The next letter I got . . . wasn't from Johnny . . . but about him. You reporters know that, though, so I guess that's all I've got to say. What? Yes . . . I'm proud of him. I know . . . not everyone's husband is a hero . . . but then . . . not everyone's husband is dead. Oh, that's all right. It was my fault . . . I shouldn't have said it that way. . . . Have I got

146

anything to say? Everything's been said . . . the papers are full of Johnny . . . you should know . . . you've been writing about him. The big words they use and the nice things important people say about him . . . there's not much I can add to that. . . . I'm just Johnny Smith's wife . . . but then I think maybe that's the most important thing of all . . . maybe that's what Johnny died for . . . . not the big words and the fine phrases . . . but the little things . . . like Sunday at Coney Island, a job to go to in the morning, the movies in the evening . . . the right to stay home and read or go for a walk in the park and hear people laughing and see them smiling . . . all the simple things that add up to life and make it worth living . . . that's what Johnny died for . . . and that's all I've got to say. I'm just Johnny Smith's wife . . . and proud of it.

(*MUSIC: Hits to close.*)

KIDNAPPED

By

JOSEPH HAYES

CAST

George Wilson

Mr. Wilson

Mrs. Wilson

Marilyn Wells

Freddie Pyle

Pete

Telephone Operator

Filling Station Attendant

Policeman

Women

KIDNAPPED

ANNOUNCER. The Radio Players of ——— School present *Kidnapped*, a radio comedy by Joseph Hayes.

(*MUSIC: Swift, lively: in and up . . . fade under.*)

ANNOUNCER. Springville has one large country club and on Saturday nights the young people hold a dance there. The house at 132 Amberton Street is all the way across town from the club, so there is sometimes a discussion about young George Wilson's taking the family car.

(*MUSIC: Out.*)

MR. WILSON (*pleasant, typical father—firm but not unkindly*). I just thought a year in college would give you some—some gumption—some get-up-and-go. I'm worried every time you drive, George, because there's nothing more dangerous than a timid driver.

GEORGE (*affable, reticent, a little weak. Nineteen*). I guess you're right at that.

MR. WILSON (*a little loud*). You don't have to agree with me!

MRS. WILSON (*mature, unruffled, positive, in a kindly way. At the moment pacifying*). Don't raise your voice, William. We're all right here in the living room and the windows are open now.

GEORGE. He's right though, Mother. I *am* a dangerous driver. Why, if I see a red light two blocks away, I want to put on the brakes. . . . I'll just have to think of another way to take Marilyn out to the club.

151

Mr. Wilson. I didn't say you *couldn't* have the car, George.

George. Oh. I thought that's what you meant.

Mr. Wilson (*irritated*). What I meant was: I wish you'd get up some spunk about you—and—and—!

Mrs. Wilson. I'll be at the Women's Auxiliary Meeting, George —playing cards. So don't worry about my getting home.

Mr. Wilson. What I can't understand, young man, is how you manage to hold a girl like Marilyn Wells!

George (*sadly*). Oh, I'm not holding her.

Mr. Wilson. No? Well, I'm not surprised.

George. Marilyn's been acting different ever since I got home from college. Sort of . . . irritable and—I guess maybe she doesn't like me any more.

Mr. Wilson. Well, what are you going to do about it?

George. Do? Oh, nothing, I guess. She just makes me mad sometimes.

Mr. Wilson. Listen, George—take the car! Take it, understand! And I don't care what happens—just so you show that girl you're not made of icewater!

Mrs. Wilson (*warningly*). Now, William, be careful!

George. Does my tie look all right?

Mr. Wilson (*a trifle fiercely*). Did you hear what I said, George?

George. Sure. You said to wreck the car if I want to just so I prove to Marilyn I'm not a drip. . . . But don't worry: I won't. Because I guess, from your viewpoint, and hers—I *am* a drip. Good night.

(*SOUND: Door opens . . . closes.*)

(*MUSIC: Bridge . . . fading into dance music and sound of voices as at dance . . . continues under.*)

Marilyn (*pleasant girlish voice*). Pick up your feet, George. This isn't a waltz.

KIDNAPPED

GEORGE. You used to think I was a good dancer.

MARILYN. I used to play Hopscotch and Skip-the-rope.

GEORGE. You mean you—you're tired of me, huh?

MARILYN. Turn, George, turn!

GEORGE. Are you, Marilyn—tired of me? Even if you haven't seen me for nearly a whole year? (*Voice changes*) Say, who are you looking for?

MARILYN. No one, George. (*Hums a snatch*) What makes you think I'm looking for someone in particular?

GEORGE. Well, you've danced enough with Freddie Pyle to make me think—

MARILYN. Oh, don't be jealous, for Pete's sake.

GEORGE. It doesn't seem right somehow to come home and find you acting so—distant—and cold—and so interested in Freddie Pyle.

MARILYN (*teasingly*). What are you going to do about it?

GEORGE. Do? Why's everyone trying to get me to *do* something? What do you want me to *do* about it?

MARILYN. *Any*thing! *Some*thing! *Any*thing!

GEORGE. Well, you just be careful, see? I might.

MARILYN. No, you won't! All you ever do is step on my feet!

GEORGE. Yeah? Well, you've been stepping on mine, too. Look at those white shoes!

MARILYN. George, people are looking at you. . . . Dance!

FREDDIE (*unpleasant, self-satisfied, twenty, fading on*). May I cut in?

GEORGE. No!

MARILYN. Of course you may, Freddie.

FREDDIE. Sorry, old man.

GEORGE. Okay. Take her! And be careful of your shoes!

MARILYN (*angry*). Oh—*oh!*

FREDDIE. What'd he mean by that?

MARILYN. George Wilson makes me so—so!—

FREDDIE. Never mind, baby. What about dancing a little closer?

(*MUSIC: Dance music merges with bridge music . . . bridge music out . . . dance music very faint under.*)

PETE (*lively, friendly, youthful, enthusiastic*). What're you doing standing out here on the porch by yourself, George?

GEORGE. Oh, hello, Pete. . . . How are you?

PETE. Freddie Pyle cutting you out, George?

GEORGE. Naw! I'm just tired.

PETE. Yeah? Boy, look at them in there—cheek to cheek!

GEORGE. Are they?

PETE. Yeah. Boy, I wouldn't let anyone dance that close to my girl.

GEORGE. What would you do?

PETE. I'd swat him!

GEORGE. You mean—

PETE. Plaster him one! Then I'd grab my girl and get outa here. That's all women understand, George—the cave-man approach!

GEORGE. But . . . all those people . . . and—

PETE. Marilyn'd love you for it.

GEORGE. She's kinda funny about things.

PETE. You sure look mad, George—mad enough to do anything.

GEORGE (*grimly*). I'm mad enough all right.

PETE. Marilyn's laughing now. Look at her.

GEORGE (*angry*). Probably at me.

PETE. Probably.

GEORGE. They can't dance around in there laughing at me!

PETE. You said it, George!

GEORGE. I've got to do something . . . like Dad said.

PETE. Now Freddie's trying a new step—they sure look happy.

KIDNAPPED

GEORGE. They can't do that!

(*SOUND: Steps receding . . . determined.*)

PETE. Hey, George. Where you goin'?

(*SOUND: Door opens and closes.*)

(*MUSIC: Dance music and voices in full . . . under.*)

GEORGE. Hey, you—

MARILYN. George!

FREDDIE. Cutting in, old man?

GEORGE. And how! This is for you, Freddie!

(*SOUND: GEORGE's fist hits FREDDIE . . . there are squeals and loud voices of exclamations and surprise . . . under.*)

(*MUSIC: Dance music out.*)

GEORGE. C'mon, Marilyn. You're going with me!

MARILYN. George Wilson! Are you crazy?

GEORGE. C'mon!

MARILYN. Let go my wrist.

GEORGE. Get out of the way, everybody!

MARILYN. George, you're hurting me!

GEORGE. Then hurry up.

MARILYN. Where are you taking me?

GEORGE. Never mind. Stop struggling.

(*SOUND: Door opens and slams. . . . Voices and exclamations fade . . . steps across gravel.*)

MARILYN. George Wilson, if you don't let me go—

GEORGE. Get in the car.

(*SOUND: Car door opens.*)

GEORGE. Get in.

MARILYN. I'll never forgive you for this.

(*SOUND: Car door slams.*)

(*MUSIC: Bridge . . . very lively, fast . . . out.*)

(*SOUND: Telephone rings . . . telephone lifted from hook.*)

MR. WILSON. Hello.

KIDNAPPED

FREDDIE (*on filter mike if possible*). Hello. Hello, Mr. Wilson. This is Freddie Pyle, I'm at the Country Club.

MR. WILSON. Yes, Freddie?

FREDDIE. I just called to tell you your son is eloping!

MR. WILSON. *What?*

FREDDIE. Eloping with Marilyn Wells. He just socked me in the jaw!

MR. WILSON. He did *what?* (*Excited*) I don't believe it! Good-bye—I mean: thanks! I mean—oh, the devil!

(*SOUND: Click of receiver on phone.*)

MR. WILSON (*mumbling to himself*). If this is some kind of a college-kid joke!—

(*SOUND: Receiver lifted from hook.*)

TELEPHONE OPERATOR (*impersonal, sharp. On filter mike if possible*). Number please.

MR. WILSON (*excited*). Hello, Operator—get me the Norton residence at—on Wilder Lane.

TELEPHONE OPERATOR. What's the number please?

MR. WILSON. Confound it, I don't *know* the number. My wife's there! Hurry! This is a matter of life or death!

TELEPHONE OPERATOR (*business-like, unexcited, sing-song*). Life or death—yessir. Hold the line.

(*MUSIC: Bridge . . . very swift . . . out.*)

(*SOUND: Car motor at high speed . . . continues under.*)

MARILYN. George, I never saw you drive this fast before.

GEORGE. I never drove this fast before . . . but it's fun!

MARILYN. Where are we going— Look out!

(*SOUND: Squeal of car brakes.*)

MARILYN. George, do you want to kill us both?

GEORGE (*calmly*). He stopped in time, didn't he?

MARILYN. Wait till my father hears of this!

GEORGE. I'm not scared of your father either.

KIDNAPPED

MARILYN. If you don't stop this car this instant, I'll jump out!

GEORGE. Oh, no, you don't!

MARILYN. Take your arm from around me! (*Screams*) Look out! Drive with two hands! You nearly went over the curb!—

GEORGE. I can't if you're going to be crazy and try to open the door.

MARILYN. Well, I won't—

GEORGE. Promise?

MARILYN. I promise. . . . Oh please, George, be careful.

GEORGE. All right then. Now I'm going to pull in up here and get some gas. If you do anything silly, you'll wish you hadn't, see!

(*SOUND: Brakes applied . . . motor comes to stop.*)

FILLING-STATION MAN (*heavy-voiced*). You better watch the way you're driving, Bud. What'll it be?

GEORGE. Six Ethyl.

MAN. Okay.

MARILYN. Mister—

GEORGE (*low*). I warn you, Marilyn!—

MAN. Yeah, Sister?

GEORGE. She doesn't want anything. Hurry it up.

MAN (*suspiciously*). Well . . . okay.

(*SOUND: Gasoline pump . . . continues under.*)

MARILYN (*low*). George, I'll never speak to you again as long as I—

GEORGE (*cocky*). Oh yes, you will.

MARILYN. What's got into you any way? You've always been so—so kind and considerate and—

GEORGE. *Meek*. Well, I'm good and tired of being *meek*.

(*SOUND: Gasoline pump out.*)

MAN. That's one-dollar, twenty-six, Bud.

GEORGE. Here.

KIDNAPPED

(*SOUND: Money being exchanged.*)

MAN. Say, Sister, you been crying?

GEORGE. What if she has!

(*SOUND: Motor starts . . . continues under.*)

MAN. This young punk been hurtin' yuh, Sister?

MARILYN (*loud*). Not *hurting* me—no, not hurting me—just *kidnapping* me!

(*SOUND: Motor races. . . . GEORGE throws it into gear . . . tires spin . . . motor recedes under.*)

MAN. Kidnap—! Say! (*Loud*) Hey! Come back here! 7–3–7–4–2. Got it.

(*SOUND: Steps across pavement . . . screen door opens and slams. . . .*)

MAN. Ohmigosh! Kidnapping—! 7–3–7–4–2.

(*SOUND: Telephone lifted from hook.*)

TELEPHONE OPERATOR (*same as before*). Number please—?

MAN. Get me police headquarters, Sister. Quick. This is an emergency!

TELEPHONE OPERATOR. Just a moment, please.

MAN. Hello! Police? I want to report a license number—no, a kidnapping. License number 7–3–7–4–2. I was just too fast for 'em! They're heading toward Warrentown. (*Fades.*)

(*MUSIC: Bridge merging with MAN's voice . . . then out.*)

(*SOUND: Women's voices.*)

WOMEN (*contrasting voices mingled a bit*).

Two no-trump.

That old hat!

Three hearts.

That husband of mine—tch, tch.

(*SOUND: Telephone ringing . . . under.*)

WOMEN. Let me tell you my recipe!

Oh, let's play cards!—

KIDNAPPED

WOMAN (*definitely above others*). The telephone's for you, Mrs. Wilson.

MRS. WILSON. For me? Thank you, Mrs. Norton. Excuse me, girls.

(*SOUND: Voices into background . . . door opens and closes . . . voices out.*)

MRS. WILSON. Hello.

MR. WILSON (*on filter mike, if possible. Very excited*). Hello, Jane! At last.

MRS. WILSON. Yes, William?

MR. WILSON. Jane, something's happened. Now get hold of yourself. Just get hold of yourself. (*He is very excited himself*) I've been trying to get you for ten minutes. It's George—!

MRS. WILSON (*alarmed*). George—?

MR. WILSON. Of course, I'm not sure, Jane—but I think George has—is—married—

MRS. WILSON (*weakly*). Mar—?

MR. WILSON. Just hold on a minute, Jane. There's someone at the door.

MRS. WILSON. William—! William!

(*SOUND: A jumble of voices on filter mike. No words can be discerned.*)

MRS. WILSON. I'm going crazy. I'm going stark, staring— (*Loud*) William, come back to the phone.

MR. WILSON (*back on phone*). It's the police, Jane.

MRS. WILSON. The *what*?

MR. WILSON. Now get hold—the police. There's been a kidnapping in town—on top of everything else. And someone's stolen our car—!

MRS. WILSON. But what about George?

MR. WILSON. They don't know. He probably found out the car was stolen so he probably didn't elope after all!

159

KIDNAPPED

MRS. WILSON. Oh, thank heavens!

MR. WILSON. So don't worry, Jane. Get one of the ladies to bring you home. . . . The police'll get the car back—and if it's kidnapping as well as larceny—the culprit'll probably get life imprisonment!

(*MUSIC: Bridge . . . swift . . . into—*)

(*SOUND: Motor at high speed under—*)

GEORGE (*singing gaily*). "Hail, hail, the gang's all here—!"

MARILYN. This is the Warrentown Road, George—where are we going?

GEORGE. Just for a nice long drive until you quiet down.

MARILYN. Well, you don't have to go so fast—!

GEORGE (*singing*). "For he's a jolly good fellow—"

(*SOUND: Police siren . . . far-off . . . approaching.*)

GEORGE. What's that?

MARILYN. A red light! A police car! Hah.

GEORGE (*dismayed*). Oh boy!

MARILYN (*singing, quite pleased*). "For he's a jolly good fellow—"

(*MUSIC: Bridge . . . merges with siren . . . then music and siren out . . . into—*)

(*SOUND: MARILYN's and GEORGE's voices mingled . . . raised in disagreement . . . jumbled—*)

GEORGE. It was just a joke, sir. I've known this girl all my life. Here's my driver's license.

MARILYN. It was kidnapping! He went mad or something and kidnapped me and—

POLICEMAN (*gruff, baffled, loud*). All right, all right. You're in the county courthouse at Warrentown and the jail's next door and there are prisoners in there trying to sleep . . . so one at a time. Now, the young lady claims she has been kidnapped.

And you say it was just a prank to prove you're a he-man. Is that it?

GEORGE (*meekly*). Sort of.

POLICE. And the state policeman who brought you in said you were doing sixty-five miles an hour on the highway!

GEORGE. It may have been that fast.

MARILYN. It was ninety at least!

POLICE. And we just received a report from Springville that there's been a kidnapping over there—and a car bearing the same license number as the one you're driving has been stolen from the Country Club there.

GEORGE. "Stolen"?

POLICE. If all this is true, you'll face a jail sentence, young feller. You're a pretty young man to be such a desperado—and you certainly don't *look* like a criminal!

GEORGE. It just didn't work, I guess. Why don't you just put me in the jail next door and forget the whole thing?

POLICE. I don't have any other choice.

MARILYN. Oh, George, don't be a dunce!

GEORGE (*surprised*). What?

POLICE. Do you have something to add, Miss?

MARILYN. But of course I do. Show him your driver's license, George. That proves it was your father's car, doesn't it? (*Cajolingly—a woman's way*) Now, Officer, you see, it was like this—it was all *my* idea. (*Very soft*) George and I are engaged, you see, and I was impulsive enough to want to get married tonight. Isn't that right, George?

GEORGE (*baffled*). If . . . you . . . say . . . so . . . Marilyn.

MARILYN (*continuing in syrupy tones*). And we had a little spat on the way, you see—just a little lovers' quarrel, wasn't it, George?

KIDNAPPED

GEORGE (*small voice*). Say, Marilyn—do you know you've got
your arm around me?

MARILYN. Isn't he sweet, Officer? (*Purring*) So you see it was
all my fault in a way and we'll be glad to pay the fine for
speeding right now if we can just— (*Fades.*)

(*MUSIC: Bridge . . . merges with MARILYN's voice . . . continues a moment . . . then out.*)

(*SOUND: Motor purring along at low speed . . . under—*)

GEORGE. You were wonderful, Marilyn. They were putty in
your hands.

MARILYN. That fine cost me my allowance for a whole month.
I hope you're satisfied—you and your masterful ideas!

GEORGE (*groaning*). Now you've changed again. Gee, I never
know where I stand with you!

(*SOUND: Motor increases speed . . . continues to increase
under—*)

MARILYN. Now don't start speeding again!

GEORGE. I'm going to speed until you say we're engaged—really
engaged, this time—

MARILYN. Oh, you men!

GEORGE. Women are worse! . . . Are we engaged?

MARILYN. George, you're speeding!

GEORGE. *Are* we?

MARILYN. Oh, yes, George—yes! I'd be afraid to say anything
else after tonight.

(*SOUND: Police siren fades in . . . approaching.*)

MARILYN. What's that?

GEORGE. Guess! Whee! She loves me! Whee!

(*SOUND: Police siren very close.*)

MARILYN. George, it's the police!

GEORGE. Who cares? You love me. Whee!

(*SOUND: Police siren in full . . . merges—*)

KIDNAPPED

*(MUSIC: In . . . merging with siren . . . up . . . then down
under final announcement—)*

ANNOUNCER. You have been listening to ———— School's presentation of *Kidnapped,* a radio play, written by Joseph Hayes
and presented by special arrangement with Samuel French,
New York.

DOORS THAT SLAM

By

WIEDER DAVID SIEVERS

(Additional dialogue by Betty Smith.)

CAST

ANNE
ERNIE
ARTHUR
ANNE'S MOTHER
BEN
NICK
PRODUCER
OFFICE GIRL
WORTHINGTON
CARNIVAL OWNER
TELEPHONE OPERATOR
MAN

DOORS THAT SLAM

(*MUSIC: Program theme way up, then out. Fade in on lively dance music which fades out into background.*)

ANNOUNCER (*over the music*). Well, folks, here it is spring again. And here we are in a little southern college town. It's a swell night. The magnolias are blooming just the way they're supposed to down here and there's that scent of jasmine and honeysuckle that you can count on this time of year. And of course the moon! We just couldn't do without the moon in this old town. There's music in the air. It's coming from that old white fraternity house down that side street. It's the last houseparty of the year and the boys spread themselves a little bit and got in Biff Baker and His Boys to supply the music. Biff and His Boys are playing music sweet and hot; mostly sweet because it's spring and near graduation and . . . oh well. . . . The girls look mighty pretty in their summer party dresses. The boys are wearing tuxedoes . . . most of them. *They* look good, too. But who cares about them? There's a lot of trading in fraternity pins going on. But we told you it's spring and it's a southern college town and there's a moon and music. And there's Anne and Ernie dancing cheek to cheek.

(*MUSIC: Up playing something sentimental but catchy: one of the song hits of the day. Down to background.*)

ERNIE (*hums a bar of the song*). Having fun, Anne?

ANNE. Uh-huh. Are you, Ernie?

ERNIE. I'm with you, aren't I?

ANNE. You're awfully sweet. (*Laughs*) Stop, silly. Don't kiss me in front of everybody.

ERNIE. Let's go look at the moon then. We haven't checked up on it in half an hour.

ARTHUR (*smooth and assured*). Mind if I cut in, Ernie?

ERNIE. You bet! Why don't you get a girl of your own, Arthur?

ANNE (*chidingly*). Now, Ernie!

ERNIE (*grudgingly*). Okay, then. One chorus.

ANNE (*laughs*).

(*MUSIC: Way up for a phrase, then down to background.*)

ARTHUR. Why do you keep ducking me, Anne?

ANNE. I do no such thing, Arthur.

ARTHUR. Everytime I look at you, you're dancing with Ernie.

ANNE. Maybe I'm stagestruck.

ARTHUR. Ernie will never be an actor.

ANNE. Ernie is an actor.

ARTHUR. Oh yeah. Here around college. But he'll never make a living at it. What I mean, a living. Now take me, Anne.

ANNE. Is this a proposal, Arthur?

ARTHUR. Could be. I'm pretty well set. I'm going into business with my dad.

ANNE. Is that his good luck or yours?

ARTHUR. Ernie's a swell feller . . .

ANNE (*breaking in*). But . . .

ARTHUR. Well, what kind of ambition is that? Actor! Work six weeks, walk the streets six months looking for another part. You can't build a home on that.

ANNE. I guess I'm the one who knows what I like.

ARTHUR. Your mother said a feller like Ernie has no right to get a girl seriously interested in him.

ANNE. My mother married whom she pleased. I'll do the same.

ARTHUR. Hold everything! What's this? Marriage? You and Ernie?

ANNE (*petulantly*). I didn't say that, Arthur. But I get so mad . . . everyone telling me what to do.

ARTHUR. Anne, I guess you know how I feel about you. I'm no glamour man like Ernie. But I think we could have a pretty swell life together.

ANNE. You're mighty sweet, Arthur, but . . .

ARTHUR. But your heart belongs to Ernie. Right?

ANNE (*with a little laugh*). I kind of guess so.

ARTHUR. Well, I won't give up until I get an invitation to a wedding.

ANNE (*laughs*).

ERNIE. Mind if I cut back in? Anne's having too good a time with you, Arthur.

ARTHUR (*disgustedly*). You would bust in, Ernie. Just when I was beginning to make a little time. (*Fading out*) Well, okay. I'll be seeing you, Anne.

ERNIE (*sorrowfully*). You can't even trust your own fraternity brother.

(*MUSIC: Up full a phrase then fade to background.*)

ANNE. Well, Ernie?

ERNIE. Well, Anne? Seems like we have some unfinished business.

ANNE. Sure 'nough. The moon.

ERNIE. Come on outside.

(*SOUND: Door opening, closing.*)

(*MUSIC: Very faint.*)

ANNE. The moon's still there, Ernie.

ERNIE. I just wanted to make sure.

ANNE. Now what remark was that about unfinished business?

ERNIE. I forgot. I was going to kiss you, wasn't I? (*Bored, yawns*) Oh well. If you insist.

ANNE. Don't go to any trouble about it.

ERNIE. No trouble. No trouble at all.

(*SOUND: Kiss.*)

ERNIE. Anne, did I ever tell you I think you're kind of nice?

ANNE. You said something like that once. However, maybe you'd better repeat it just to make sure.

ERNIE. Anne, I think you're kind of nice.

ANNE. I think you're kind of nice too, Ernie.

ERNIE. Check?

ANNE. Check.

(*SOUND: Kiss.*)

(*MUSIC: Runs out along about here.*)

ERNIE. Well, darling, thus endeth a college course.

ANNE. And thus beginneth a bigger and better career.

ERNIE. They say acting's a tough profession.

ANNE. Not if you're good.

ERNIE. I'd rather act than do anything else in the world.

ANNE. Do you like acting better than me?

ERNIE. That's different.

ANNE (*laughs*). I know.

ERNIE. There's something about the theatre. . . . It gets me everytime I walk backstage and the theatre's empty and I look around at the flats standing against the wall and see the dusty sunlight slanting down from somewhere.

ANNE (*abruptly*). Arthur's going into business with his father.

ERNIE (*coming out of his dream*). Who? Oh! Arthur. Yes, Anne, the theatre's pretty wonderful to me but not half as wonderful as you.

(*MUSIC: Now the music comes up playing "The Sweetheart of Sigma Chi."*)

ERNIE. Oh Anne, I'll never forget those wonderful autumn days and the walks we took out into the country.

ANNE. When we should have been in the library studying.

ERNIE. Perfect days like that will never come again.

ANNE (*hums a line from "The Sweetheart of Sigma Chi"*). I wonder where we'll be a year from now?

ERNIE. In New York. And I'll be playing the lead in a smash hit.

ANNE. And expecting me to come backstage every night to tell you how good you were.

ERNIE (*acting it out*). How were we tonight, Mrs. Farrell?

ANNE. Wonderful, Mr. Farrell. There's a gang of women waiting for your autograph.

ERNIE. What a bore. Let's sneak out the back way, grab a bite to eat and then go home to the children.

ANNE. Children? Why didn't you tell me we have children?

ERNIE. We have Junior, a sourpuss like his old man and a little girl who is just as darling as her mother.

(*Both laugh.*)

ANNE. But seriously, dear, suppose one of us has . . . what they call a change of heart?

ERNIE. We'll be very honest with each other. I'd want you to tell me if you ever stopped caring for me.

ANNE. I promise. And you must tell me.

ERNIE. I promise. Mind if I seal that with a kiss, Miss Anne Barton?

ANNE. The Lord helps those who help themselves, Mr. Farrell.

(*SOUND: Kiss.*)

(*MUSIC: Goes out just before last speech.*)

ERNIE. Anne, let's announce our engagement tonight. It's our last houseparty.

ANNE (*quickly*). Oh no. That's so final.

ERNIE. Well, so is our love.

(*MUSIC: Lively dance tune comes in suddenly.*)

ANNE. Let's dance. I love that song.

ERNIE. Anne, are you trying to avoid the issue?

ANNE. Ernie, our promises are enough. Then if things didn't turn out right, we wouldn't have our friends feeling sorry for us.

ERNIE. All right, dear. We won't announce it then. But I'll work hard and get someplace. . . . (*Frightened*) Oh, Anne, you will wait for me, won't you?

ANNE. I'll . . . (*Hesitates*) I'll wait.

ERNIE. The boys expect me to announce our engagement tonight.

ANNE. Oh, you can get out of it.

ERNIE. Kiss me, Anne, tell me you love me.

ANNE. Of course, Ernie.

ERNIE. Put your arms around me . . .

ANNE. There.

(*SOUND: Door opens.*)

(*MUSIC: Up a few bars then down.*)

ARTHUR. Anne . . .

ANNE (*startled*). Arthur!

ARTHUR. This is supposed to be a *dance*, you know, Ernie.

ERNIE. I guess I've got a right to kiss my fiancée, Arthur.

ARTHUR. Engaged? You two? You sure can keep a secret, Anne.

ANNE (*angrily*). Ernie spoke out of turn. Nothing definite has been settled.

ARTHUR. No wedding bells for a while? Good.

ERNIE. Anne can't support me without a job and vice versa. But after I give Broadway a break, I'll come back hoping the little woman is still waiting for me.

ARTHUR. What a chance you're taking!

ERNIE. Anne will wait.

ARTHUR. What I mean . . . actors are a dime a dozen.

DOORS THAT SLAM

ANNE. Not like Ernie.

ERNIE. Thanks, Anne.

ANNE. Oh, Ernie, do that speech for me again. You know, the one from the last play?

ERNIE. What's the cue?

ANNE (*very commonplace*). Good shepherd tell what 'tis to love.

ERNIE (*recites very well*). It is to be all made of fantasy,
All made of passion and all made of wishes;
All adoration, duty and observance.

(*MUSIC: Up on "Sweetheart of Sigma Chi."*)

ERNIE. All humbleness, all patience and impatience.
All purity, all trial, all observance.

ANNE. Oh, Ernie!

(*MUSIC: "Sigma Chi" out. Fade in "Pomp and Circumstance."
Fade to:*)

DEAN (*pompously*). Ernest Richard Farrell, President of Phi Beta Kappa Society, member of the student Council, prominent in dramatics. . . . (*Fades out.*)

(*MUSIC: Up and then fade out for:*)

PRESIDENT. . . . another commencement. And now we send these young people out to fulfil their destiny in a troubled world. We do so with profound conviction that they will reflect credit on their Alma Mater. So now, we of this great University . . . (*Fade out.*)

(*MUSIC: Pompous music up and fade into:*)

(*SOUND: Railroad station bells, etc.*)

ANNE. Goodbye, darling.

ERNIE. Write to me every day, Anne. I love you so terribly. Who do you love?

ANNE. I love Mr. Ernest Farrell, who's going to be a great actor.

DISPATCHER. All 'board!

173

ERNIE. Goodbye, sweet. Remember you're coming to New York Christmas.

ANNE. Think of me every minute. And write! Write!

(*SOUND: Train up and fade away.*)

ANNE (*slight sob*).

ARTHUR. Hello, Anne. Been seeing Ernie off?

ANNE. Arthur! Why yes!

ARTHUR. I've got my car outside. Want a ride home?

ANNE. No thank you.

ARTHUR (*fading out*). Well, keep the home fires burning.

ANNE (*raising her voice*). Arthur! Wait!

(*MUSIC: Transition. A few bars of "Sigma Chi," some of "Pomp and Circumstance" and fade into jazzy New York music like "Forty-second Street" or "Skyscraper Suite."*)

ERNIE. Yes sir. And I made Phi Beta Kappa and got my name on the cup for the best acting at school and . . .

PRODUCER (*hard-boiled New Yorker*). Professional experience?

ERNIE. I played two summers ago at the Old Barn Playhouse.

PRODUCER. Professional experience?

ERNIE. I'll take anything you've got. Just let me read.

PRODUCER. Not the type.

ERNIE. I look different under makeup.

PRODUCER. I'll take your name. Come back in a month.

ERNIE. Thank you.

(*MUSIC: New York music. Transition.*)

ERNIE. Pardon me, ma'am. I'm Ernest Farrell. I want to see Mr. Haskell about some work.

OFFICE GIRL. Is it about casting?

ERNIE. Well, yes.

OFFICE GIRL. Sorry. Mr. Haskell isn't casting just now.

ERNIE. But that's what you said three weeks ago. And since then he put a play in rehearsal and . . .

OFFICE GIRL. Sorry. You're not the type.

ERNIE. Tell me what type he wants. I'll be it.

OFFICE GIRL. If you'll leave your address . . .

ERNIE. That's what they all tell me.

OFFICE GIRL. Sorry. Next.

BEN. I'm Ben Osborne. Remember?

OFFICE GIRL. Mr. Haskell isn't casting just now. If you'll leave your address. . . .

BEN. Forget the oil. See you again, sister.

OFFICE GIRL. Ben, that fellow that just walked out. Name of Ernest Farrell. I don't think he can take it. He looks like such a nice kid. Fresh from college, too.

BEN. Say no more. I'll wise him up about this show business. (*Fading out*) But it's a favor to you. Keep that in mind when Haskell's casting again.

OFFICE GIRL. I'll do that.

(*MUSIC: Transition music.*)

BEN. Pardon me. I've seen you around the casting offices. My name's Ben Osborne.

ERNIE. I've seen you around too. I'm Ernie Farrell.

BEN. Any luck?

ERNIE. No. And you?

BEN. Nothing. I haven't had a part in three years.

ERNIE. Three years! I'm discouraged after looking five months. But I need a job bad because I'm going to get married.

BEN (*cynically*). Once I thought I was going to get married.

ERNIE. Anne's willing to wait for me.

BEN. Tell it to Equity. Mine was willing to wait, too. (*Laughs*) Waiting for Lefty. (*Laughs.*)

ERNIE. My girl's different.

BEN. Listen, feller, most of us lost our girls so long ago that we're monks as well as actors.

ERNIE. No. Anne's waiting for me.

BEN (*gently*). Have it you own way, kid. Hear from her often?

ERNIE. Every day . . . until about three weeks ago. I wonder why she doesn't write.

BEN. Busy maybe.

ERNIE. Well, she's coming up here for Christmas and I guess that will be worth more than letters.

BEN. Sure, sure.

(*MUSIC: New York music up and blend into "Sigma Chi," out for:*)

ANNE. But Arthur, I don't want to go to the show tonight.

ARTHUR. You put in a word for me, Mrs. Barton.

MRS. BARTON. Now, Anne dear, it will do you good to go out with Arthur.

ANNE. But I've got to write to Ernie. It's nearly three weeks since I wrote, Mother.

MRS. BARTON. I should think you'd be tired writing letters.

ARTHUR. Aw come on, Anne. You can write Sunday.

MRS. BARTON. Ernie's a nice boy and I haven't got a thing against him, Anne. But I'm sure *he's* not sitting in New York twiddling his thumbs.

ANNE. But it might make him feel bad if I went out.

ARTHUR. Not with an old fraternity brother of his. What do you say, Mrs. Barton?

MRS. BARTON. I just wouldn't mention it, Anne, when I wrote. A small thing like that.

ARTHUR. Aw come on, Anne. I'm lonesome.

ANNE. Well, it is just a movie. Okay, Arthur.

MRS. BARTON. I'm sure you're being very sensible, Anne. (*Fading*) Have a good time, children.

(*MUSIC: New York music up and crashes to a climax.*)

DOORS THAT SLAM

ERNIE (*wearily and without inspiration*). It is to be all made of fantasy. All made of passion and all made of wishes.

(*SOUND: Knock on door.*)

ERNIE (*eagerly*). Come in!

(*SOUND: Door opening, closing.*)

BEN. Hello, Ernie.

ERNIE (*disappointed*). Oh, Ben. Hello.

BEN. What's the matter?

ERNIE. I just thought it was the landlady with a letter from Anne.

BEN. Haven't you heard from her yet?

ERNIE. No.

BEN. Cheer up. I've got good news. I heard Worthington needs five British soldiers for his new musical. I'm on my way there now. Want to come along?

ERNIE. You bet.

(*SOUND: Street noises up and out.*)

(*MUSIC: Few bars military music.*)

(*SOUND: Fade in crowd murmuring.*)

ERNIE. You must have been wrong, Ben.

BEN. That's what I was told . . . that he needed five soldiers.

ERNIE. But there must be two hundred here.

BEN. We're not the only actors out of a job.

WORTHINGTON (*smooth, oily*). All right. All right. Line up.

(*SOUND: Murmur up, excited.*)

ERNIE. My name is Farrell. If you'll just let me read the part . . .

WORTHINGTON. What part? The soldiers have no lines. Quiet!

(*SOUND: Murmur dies down.*)

WORTHINGTON. All right now. I want five British soldiers.

ERNIE. If you'll give me a chance, Mr. Worthington . . .

WORTHINGTON. How tall are you, Farrell?

ERNIE. Five feet nine, sir, but . . .

WORTHINGTON. Too short. All of you over six feet step forward.

(*SOUND: Steps forward, murmur.*)

WORTHINGTON. You'll do. And you and you and you. The rest of you . . .

ERNIE (*anxiously*). Yes?

WORTHINGTON. Thanks for coming.

(*SOUND: Indignant murmur.*)

WORTHINGTON. Quiet!

ERNIE. But, Mr. Worthington . . .

WORTHINGTON. No more casting today. Now you soldiers march across the stage. Let's see what we have here.

(*SOUND: Five men marching.*)

ERNIE. Mr. Worthington! Wait!

(*SOUND: Stumble and crash.*)

(*SOUND: Derisive laughter.*)

BEN. Ernie! Did you hurt yourself stumbling over that chair?

ERNIE. I'm all right, Ben. Let's go.

WORTHINGTON. Just a moment. You! What's your name again?

ERNIE. Me? Ernie Farrell.

WORTINGTON. I just got an idea. Little soldier marching behind five big ones. Perfect marching. Little soldier stumbles. Good for a laugh. We'll write in some lines for you. Report for rehearsal ten o'clock tomorrow morning. Twenty-five a week. That's all.

(*SOUND: Door opens, closes.*)

ERNIE. What does it mean, Ben?

BEN. It means you're in. All you got to do is pay Equity fifty dollars and you're an actor.

ERNIE. I can hardly believe it. Where's a phone booth? I've got to call Anne.

BEN. She might be out having her hair washed or something.

178

Why don't you wait until tonight? Rates are cheaper then.

ERNIE. That's right. Gee, Ben, I'm sorry you didn't get a part.

BEN. Forget it. Say, you couldn't loan me two bits, could you?

(*MUSIC: City music up and then transition: small town music.*)

(*SOUND: Music out, phone rings. Receiver off hook.*)

MRS. BARTON. Hello? The Barton residence.

OPERATOR. Go ahead, New York. Here's your party.

ERNIE. Hello, Mrs. Barton. This is Ernie Farrell. How are you and may I speak to Anne, please?

MRS. BARTON. Ernie! Well! I'd never recognize your voice. When the phone rang and the operator said long distance calling, I said to myself, now who could be calling after eleven o'clock?

ERNIE. I just got three minutes. Could I speak to Anne, please?

MRS. BARTON (*frigidly*). Anne isn't home. She went out with Arthur Danielson.

ERNIE. With Arthur? Do you know when she *will* be home?

(*SOUND: Door opens.*)

MRS. BARTON. No, I don't, Ernie.

ANNE. Ernie? Let me take it, Mother. (*Into phone*) Hello, Ernie.

ERNIE. Hello, darling. Gee, it's good to hear your voice again.

ANNE. I just got home. I hardly recognized your voice. It's been almost six months since I heard it.

ERNIE. I've got a job, Anne.

ANNE. Oh, Ernie, that's wonderful!

ERNIE. Why haven't you written?

ANNE. I've been so terribly busy. Sweet of you to call me up and tell me about the job.

ERNIE. I'll have enough money to take you around when you come up here for Christmas.

ANNE. Ernie, I won't be able to make it. My grandmother's coming. I was going to write and tell you.

ERNIE. But, Anne, you promised. . . .

ANNE. I'm sorry.

ERNIE. You've got to come. I'm so lonesome for you.

ANNE. But grandmother expects me to be here Christmas.

ERNIE. So does Arthur Danielson, I guess.

ANNE. Don't let's fight, Ernie.

ERNIE. I guess you think I don't know about little Arthur.

ANNE. Don't be silly. My grandmother *is* coming.

ERNIE. Who are you going to marry? Me or your grandmother?

OPERATOR. Your three minutes are up.

ANNE. Goodbye, Ernie.

ERNIE (*frantically*). Anne! Anne!

(*SOUND: Phone hung up.*)

(*MUSIC: "Sweetheart of Sigma Chi" comes up and fades into New York music. Out for:*)

BEN. What's the word, Ernie?

ERNIE. She can't make it, Ben. Her grandmother's coming.

BEN. At least she thought up a new angle.

ERNIE. But I've got to see her. That's why I wanted a job so bad . . . to have her with me.

BEN. Six months is a long time, Ernie. Even if she's all you say.

ERNIE. Ben, do you thing she's beginning to forget me?

BEN. It's happened before. There's always another fellow waiting around.

ERNIE (*whispers*). Arthur Danielson! (*Louder*) I've got to go down to North Carolina to see her.

BEN. What will you use for money?

ERNIE. I'll thumb a ride down.

BEN. But you'll lose your job. You waited five months for this chance.

ERNIE. To heck with the job. I can't lose Anne.

BEN. Well, it's your funeral, Ernie. (*Snaps his fingers*) Say! Maybe Worthington will give me your job. Oh boy!

(*SOUND: Traffic noises way up and out for:*)

(*MUSIC: Few bars of "Sigma Chi."*)

ANNE. You poor thing! And when you got to Richmond were you able to bum another ride, Ernie?

ERNIE. Not right away, Anne.

ANNE (*sympathetically*). Ernie!

ERNIE. Let's forget my trip. I'm actually here and with you . . . and oh, darling, I missed you so much.

ANNE. I missed you too. But you were very foolish to leave New York just when you got a break.

ERNIE. I felt I was losing you.

ANNE. Mother said you were very foolish to give up a good job just because I happened to go to the show with Arthur.

ERNIE. I'll get a job here for a while just to be near you. Then when I have enough money saved we'll marry and go to New York together. No more separations.

ANNE. Darling, I doubt if you can get a job here.

ERNIE. You don't know me. Just give me three weeks. I'll have a job.

ANNE. Three weeks?

ERNIE. Three weeks.

(*MUSIC: Up to take care of a transition of three weeks.*)

ANNE (*scornfully*). Three weeks! Well, the time's up. I told you you couldn't find a job down here.

ERNIE. Anne, I tried every store and every filling station.

ANNE. Ernie, why don't you go back to New York?

ERNIE. I will, Anne. If you'll come with me.

ANNE. What would we live on?

ERNIE. I'd find something to do.

ANNE. This isn't what we planned is it, Ernie?

ERNIE. Give me a chance, Anne.

ANNE. I can't believe it. Last June you were on top of the world and now you're practically down and out.

ERNIE. You're not much of a help.

ANNE. Oh, let's stop squabbling and get some thing to eat.

ERNIE. Could you stand hamburgers?

ANNE. If that's all you can afford.

ERNIE. This will seem like slumming to you, then.

ANNE. Oh, Ernie, stop being so touchy.

(*SOUND: Door opening, closing.*)

NICK (*a Greek, tough but kind*). What'll you have, folks?

ANNE. Could I see a menu?

NICK. What for, Miss? You know all we got is hamburgers and cokes, beer and pop.

ANNE. Oh, I don't know what I want.

NICK. Got a job yet, Ernie?

ERNIE. Not yet, Nick.

NICK. You will . . . college education and all. Especially since you got one of them keys.

ERNIE. Yeah. That's a Phi Beta Kappa key, Nick.

NICK. I'd give anything for one of those. You've certainly got to be educated these days.

ERNIE. Educated and lucky besides.

NICK. Wish I could exchange places with you, Ernie.

ERNIE. Okay, Nick. Give me that apron you're wearing.

NICK. But you can't give me your education. See what I mean? You got something nobody can take away from you.

ERNIE. But you got something, too, Nick. A steady job and maybe a wife.

NICK. I got a wife and four kids too. Lucky? Nuts!

182

DOORS THAT SLAM

ANNE. When you philosophers get through, I'll take a hamburger and coke, I guess.

ERNIE. The same for me.

NICK. Okey doke. Onions?

ERNIE (*whispers*). Anne, let's take our hamburgers and eat 'em in the park. It's such a swell night and I haven't held you in my arms in such a long time.

ANNE. Oh, Ernie, we've been walking all night. My feet are killing me. And the park's way out of the way. Some other time, Ernie.

ERNIE (*sighs*). Okay. (*Calls*) Hey, Nick! Put plenty of onions on mine.

(*MUSIC: Up to take care of a transition. Then fade out.*)

ERNIE. If you'll just give me a chance. Any kind of work.

MAN. Sorry, kid.

ERNIE. I'll do anything, sweep up . . .

MAN. Look! I'm hardly getting by myself.

ERNIE. Do you know any place I could get a job?

MAN. The movie place needed an usher.

ERNIE. The boss' son took that job.

MAN. The grocery store . . .

ERNIE. Laying off men.

MAN. Nothing here.

ERNIE. Listen! I've had twenty doors slammed in my face this past week. Before you slam your door, give me a chance. I'm just an ordinary guy and I'm in love with a girl and I want to marry her and settle down. Is there anything unreasonable about that?

(*SOUND: Door slams loudly.*)

(*MUSIC: Up to a climax, then out.*)

(*SOUND: Carnival noises.*)

ERNIE. I know I can do it, Mister. Give me a chance.

CARNIVAL MAN (*whiskey voice*). But it ain't much of a job. Ten bucks a week. College feller like you rates more.

ERNIE. I'll be glad to have the job.

CARNIVAL MAN. Let's see how good you are. I'll give you the speil. We exhibit the darin' fac's of life, ten cents, adults only.

ERNIE. Not the real facts?

CARNIVAL MAN. It's nothin' but a bunch of bottles but it sure packs 'em in. Let's hear you give it a whirl.

ERNIE (*hesitantly as he clears his throat*). Ladies and . . . I mean . . . step up, folks.

CARNIVAL MAN. You'll have to do better than that.

(*SOUND: Carnival noises up and calliope added.*)

(*SOUND: People at a carnival.*)

ERNIE. If you'll just let me have your attention . . . er . . . er . . . in this tent we have a very interesting exhibit . . . uh . . .

CARNIVAL MAN (*hoarse whisper*). Give it more guts.

ERNIE (*trying harder*). We have here the daring facts of life for only ten cents. You've never seen an exhibit like this before.

CARNIVAL MAN. Get going. They're walking away.

ERNIE (*with more assurance*). Step this way, folks, for the big show. No minors will be admitted to this daring show which tells all, knows all and shows all. What makes the world go round? Why ever since Eve . . .

CARNIVAL MAN. Now you're hitting it, Ernie.

ERNIE (*now at his best*). Step this way, ladies and gents, for this sensational exhibit of the actual true facts of life. Nothing held back, for only ten cents . . . ten cents . . . (*Fading*) two nickels, one dime . . . I tell you ladies and . . .

(*SOUND: All carnival sounds up drowning out everything.*)

DOORS THAT SLAM

(*MUSIC: Calliope up.*)

(*Everything fade out for:*)

ERNIE (*fading in. His voice is hoarse*). Anne! Anne darling! I've got a job at last, sweetheart.

ANNE. Ernie! What's the matter with your voice?

ERNIE (*his voice slowly comes back to normal during the ensuing speeches*). I guess I wore it out.

ANNE. What kind of a job, Ernie?

ERNIE. Carnival barker. Ten dollars a week.

ANNE (*distastefully*). Barker?

ERNIE. Well, it's a start in show business.

ANNE (*scornfully*). Wouldn't your mother be proud of you if she knew?

ERNIE. What's wrong with you, Anne?

ANNE. I don't know what's the matter, Ernie. I should be very happy and congratulate you.

ERNIE. That's more like it. Listen! Let's go out and celebrate.

ANNE. But, Ernie, I have a date.

ERNIE. With who?

ANNE. Arthur Danielson.

ERNIE. That dope!

ANNE. Don't be jealous.

ERNIE. Jealous? I'm insulted. You just break that date.

ANNE. But I couldn't, Ernie. He travels for his father and only has Saturday night off. I couldn't play such a dirty trick on him.

ERNIE (*quietly*). What about playing it on me?

ANNE. Must I go into a convent just because Ernie Farrell has a job with a carnival?

ERNIE. What's wrong with a carnival?

ANNE. Nothing. And there's nothing wrong with my having a date with Arthur either. You're unreasonable, Ernie.

ERNIE. Because I expect my fiancée to celebrate with me?

ANNE. We can celebrate tomorrow night, Ernie.

ERNIE. We won't celebrate at all. You can have that time free to date little Arthur. Goodbye!

(*SOUND: Door slams.*)

ANNE (*calls out*). Ernie!

(*SOUND: Door opens.*)

ERNIE (*hopefully*). You want to reconsider this matter?

ANNE (*gently*). Sit down, Ernie. I want to tell you something.

ERNIE. Oh, Anne, don't keep that date with Arthur.

ANNE. We used to be such awfully good friends, Ernie. But lately we haven't been getting along so well.

ERNIE. Oh, Anne, it's just that I haven't a job and you see so much of Arthur.

ANNE. Ernie, remember last June?

(*MUSIC: Comes up softly on "The Sweetheart of Sigma Chi."*)

ANNE. You made me promise to tell you if . . .

ERNIE. Anne, Anne, what are you trying to say?

ANNE. Ernie, you're the finest boy I ever knew but . . .

ERNIE. Tell me. Please tell me, Anne.

ANNE. Ernie, I don't think we love each other any more.

ERNIE. I love you. More than ever.

ANNE (*gently*). I'm sorry, dear. I mean I'm not in love with you any more.

ERNIE. Anne, you're just saying that because you're angry with me.

ANNE. No, dear. I guess I was in love with you last spring. But something kept telling me it wouldn't work out.

ERNIE. That's why you wouldn't let me announce our engagement.

ANNE. I thought if you went away, I'd find out whether I

really loved you or not. Oh, I know it seems cruel. But I had to be sure.

ERNIE. And of course, Arthur was around all the time.

ANNE. I wish I had written and told you. It would have been easier for both of us.

ERNIE. Anne, is it Arthur? Tell me.

ANNE. Well, Arthur and I . . . we seem to get along better and . . . Oh, Ernie, things like that just happen. People change. Ernie . . .

ERNIE. Don't say any more for awhile. Let me get my bearings. I can't believe it. We were so much in love. I thought you loved me. I guess it was just wishful thinking. (*Sighs*) Thus endeth a love affair.

ANNE. I wouldn't have hurt you for the world. Please don't hate me, Ernie.

ERNIE. I loved you too much ever to hate you. It's this crazy world that slams the door in the face of young people who want to get married and make a home. By the time you can afford to get married these days all the wonderful years of being young have passed by.

ANNE. I know. That's why I can't wait, dear.

ERNIE. If I could have gotten a good job doing what I'm trained to do, I could have made you love me somehow.

ANNE. I'm sorry you did give up that job in New York.

ERNIE. I'll get another some day.

ANNE. Here's your fraternity pin back, Ernie. I loved wearing it.

ERNIE. Oh, Anne. . . .

ANNE. I guess there isn't much more to say.

ERNIE. Will you kiss me goodbye, Anne?

ANNE. Of course, dear.

ERNIE (*whispers*). Dear.

(*MUSIC: "Sigma Chi" up louder for a phrase, then down to background for:*)

ANNE (*with a catch in her voice*). Oh, Ernie, you're so sweet. Please believe me. I still want to be your friend. Will you write to me once in a while?

ERNIE. Sure. I'll send you my first New York theatre program autographed.

ANNE. It's better this way.

(*MUSIC: "Sigma Chi" out.*)

ERNIE. Sure it's better. Only I wish I could be happy about it.

ANNE. I hope you'll think of me now and then.

ERNIE. I will. You were the first girl I ever loved. You were part of a very happy time of my life.

ANNE. That's your part in my life too.

ERNIE. I'll think of you every time I hear sweet music.

ANNE. Thank you, dear.

ERNIE. Well, goodbye, Anne.

ANNE. Goodbye, Ernie, and best of luck. You'll get there, I know.

ERNIE. But you don't want to get there with me. Right?

ANNE. Ernie, don't let's part quarrelling.

ERNIE. I'm sorry, Anne.

ANNE. I know this is all for the best. But somehow I want to cry.

ERNIE. Goodbye, dear.

(*SOUND: Door closes.*)

(*MUSIC: "Sigma Chi" up to a grand climax, then fade out. New music comes up, something sharp and modern.*)

(*SOUND:Footsteps along a street.*)

(*SOUND: Door opens, shuts.*)

ERNIE. Hi, Nick.

NICK. Hi there, Ernie. Where's the little girl tonight?

ERNIE. You mean Miss Anne Barton, the girl who was so crazy about me that she couldn't wait?

NICK. I don't get you, Ernie.

ERNIE. Anne and I are through, Nick.

NICK. No kidding!

ERNIE. That's right.

NICK. What happened?

ERNIE. I couldn't afford to love. Didn't have enough money.

NICK. I was like you once. In love and how! I got over it.

ERNIE. And probably forgot the next girl too.

NICK. Yeah. We all forget.

ERNIE. Pardon me for feeling like I'm the first guy it ever happened to.

NICK. I know you'll get over it, Ernie.

ERNIE. I'm over it now, see? Ask me how Anne is. Go ahead, Nick.

NICK. How's Anne?

ERNIE. Anne who?

NICK. That's the way to talk.

ERNIE. See this clipping, Nick?

NICK. Let's see. Hm. . . . It's about a show.

ERNIE. "The Lady and the Grenadier." Opened last night in New York. Smash hit. Will run a year.

NICK. Is that good?

ERNIE. Good enough. See this?

NICK (reads). Sixth Grenadier, Ben Osborne.

ERNIE. That's me, Nick.

NICK. No!

ERNIE. It would have been me. Only I couldn't do without that girl.

NICK. Don't let it get you down. You're going to be a big

shot some day. College education and Phi . . . whatever that key means. You'll make it, Ernie.

ERNIE. Yes, Nick, I know I will. But in the meantime, do you know anyone who wants to hire a Phi Bete cheap?

NICK. Forget that dumb talk. What do you want to eat?

ERNIE. How about some beer on credit?

NICK. I'd like to, Ernie. Only the boss would ketch me.

ERNIE. Come on, Nick. I'll pay you out of my future.

NICK. I can't take a chance, Ernie.

ERNIE. Tell you what I'll do. You like this Phi Bete key, don't you?

NICK. You bet!

ERNIE. I'll give it to you for eight bottles of beer.

NICK. Aw, you don't want to part with that, Ernie.

ERNIE. Yes I do. For some good, cool beer. How about it? I'd like to start getting drunk in a slow kind of way.

NICK. Well okey dokey, if that's what you want.

ERNIE. Here's the golden key, my friend. *In hoc signo vinces.* You are now a member in good standing. Wrap my beer up good.

NICK. Okay, Ernie. But don't you get down in the dumps. You got the stuff. I know it. You'll get there.

ERNIE. Sure, Nick. I'm on my way there now. But to get really started, I had to give up something that I wanted more than getting there.

NICK. Lotsa dames in the world.

(*SOUND: Clink of bottles wrapped up and paper.*)

NICK. Here's your beer. All wrapped up.

ERNIE. Thank you, my friend. I'll be seeing you. If Jake Shubert asks for me, tell him I'm on my way back to Broadway. So long.

NICK. So long.

DOORS THAT SLAM

(*SOUND: Door opens, closes.*)

NICK (*musing*). Nutty kind of a guy.

(*SOUND: Cash register rings up.*)

NICK. But that's sure a pretty gold key.

(*MUSIC: Up.*)

SMALL TOWN EDITOR

By

ANTHONY WAYNE

CAST

JEFF NORRIS
LEILA
BUTTONS
VIC
JOE MORRIS
MIKE
A MINISTER
MR. FULTON
A TELEGRAPH BOY

SMALL TOWN EDITOR

ACT I

LEILA. Hello, Buttons. Say! Didn't I see you swimming in the river yesterday?

(*SOUND: Opening and slamming screen door.*)

BUTTONS (*He's about 12 years old*). Hey, Leila! Shush! Do you have to tell everybody? Where's the Boss? I gotta see him.

LEILA. Anything I could do?

BUTTONS (*very serious*). No . . . I'm afraid not. This has got to do with the circulation of the paper.

LEILA. Well, maybe you'd better see Joe then.

BUTTONS. No, I think the Boss'd wanta know 'bout this hisself.

LEILA. All right, Mr. Norris ought to . . . here he comes now!

(*SOUND: Opening door.*)

JEFF (*he's a country editor about 60*). Hello there, Buttons . . . get all your papers delivered this morning?

BUTTONS. Sure thing, Boss.

LEILA. Good morning, Mr. Norris.

JEFF. Mornin', Leila. Joe here?

LEILA. No, he's down at Mark's.

JEFF. Oh yeah,— Say, Buttons, isn't it 'bout time fer you to be gettin' off to school?

BUTTONS. Yeah . . . but we got somethin' serious with the circulation.

JEFF (*indulgently*). Have we?

BUTTONS. This morning when I delivered Mrs. Murphy's paper, I give her her bill for the month.

JEFF. Yes.

BUTTONS. She takes one look at it an' says: "You tell old Jeff Norris I ain't pay'n' this bill."

JEFF. Ummmmm. Whatsa matter with her this time, Buttons?

BUTTONS. She's sore about this piece in the paper.

JEFF. Wait'll I get my specs on. Uuuummm. Let's see. "The ladies of the Shamrock Society sponsored a dance at Hibernian Hall last night. The Grand finale was a colorful affair concluding with a real old-fashioned Irish jag." Jag! (*Starts laughing*) Ha! Ha!—Jag, eh?

BUTTONS (*troubled*). But Boss, she won't pay.

JEFF. Listen, Buttons, just stop leavin' the *Banner* at her house next week. Won't be three days 'fore she'll pay up.

BUTTONS. Okay, Boss.

JEFF. An' now, you'd better skiddaddle off to school.

BUTTONS. Aw, let me help Mike in the press room.

JEFF. Say! I thought you wanted to be a newspaper man some day?

BUTTONS. I do— But they don't teach ya nothin' about newspapers.

JEFF. But they teach ya to read and write, to appreciate all the best things that smarter men than me have thought up.

BUTTONS. There ain't no smarter men than you!

JEFF. Now, Buttons, my son Joe went to college, an' some day you will too, if you get your lessons. But you gotta study. So, off with you!

BUTTONS. Kin I come back after school?

JEFF. Sure, but hurry up. You'll be late.

BUTTONS. Okay, so long!

(*SOUND: Screen door opens and slams.*)

LEILA. That boy certainly worships you, Mr. Norris.

JEFF. Poor little homeless rascal. He's almost like my own son.

LEILA. Carl Tansey was in this morning carrying on something awful.

JEFF. Yes? What about?

LEILA. We printed an announcement of his death in the paper the other day.

JEFF. We did? . . . Humph! . . . Well, put his name in the "Births" tomorrow and give him a fresh start.

LEILA (*chuckling*). I'll tell him.

(*SOUND: Screen door slamming.*)

VIC (*a farmer*). Mornin', Jeff!

JEFF. Hi there, Vic. What brings you to town?

VIC. Well . . . I'm figurin' on runnin' a cattle auction next week, an' I'd like to trade ya fer an ad in yer paper.

JEFF. Well, whatcha got to trade, Vic?

(*SOUND: Screen door slamming.*)

JOE. Did I hear something about trading?

JEFF (*guiltily*). Oh, oh. . . . I'm in for it.

VIC. What's the matter?

JEFF. Well, Vic, my son Joe here, he's got the paper in tow now. He sells the advertising.

VIC. But I've dealt with you for years, Jeff.

JOE. And the paper's been in debt for years too, Vic. The *Banner* has to make a little money. And we can't trade space.

VIC. But I ain't got no money.

JEFF (*pleading*). Why not make a trade with Vic just this once, Joe?

JOE. Now, Dad! . . . Listen, Vic, you'll have money after the auction. Let us run your ad and you pay us after the cattle are sold. How's that?

VIC. Waal . . . that's all right with me.

JOE. Fine. Then we'll run this in to-morrow's paper.

VIC. All right. So long, Jeff.

JEFF. So long, Vic.

(*SOUND: Screen door slams.*)

JOE (*mildly reprimanding*). Well, Dad, . . . I thought I was to be business manager of the *Banner*.

JEFF (*a little sheepish*). I . . . I'm sorry, Joe. I just been runnin' this old sheet alone so long . . . I forgot.

JOE. Honestly, Dad, I don't know how you've managed to stay in business all these years.

JEFF. Well, a little trade here for groceries and a little one there for clothes, an' I managed to get on.

JOE. You got on because you're the best darned editor in the United States.

JEFF (*slightly embarrassed*). N-naw . . . I named *you* after the best one . . . Joseph Pulitzer! I always hoped you'd want to write, Joe.

JOE. Not on your life. The business end's where the money's made.

JEFF. Yeah . . . I s'pose you're right. Humph. Funny! Only time I ever thought much about money was when I wanted to send you to college.

JOE. I'm going to pay you back for that too, Dad.

JEFF. I got all my pay in the letters you wrote me. Son, you got a gift fer writin'.

JOE. Now, now . . . don't go trying to make an editor out of me again.

JEFF (*laughing*). All right . . . it'll come in time. You can't keep a Norris from pourin' his thoughts into print. (*Changing the subject.*) What kind of ad did Marks give you?

JOE. A two page spread.

JEFF. Good for you! By golly, I'm proud of you, Joe. (*Calling*) You see, Leila . . . that's what college does for you.

LEILA (*off mike*). I often wondered what it did, Mr. Norris.

JEFF (*laughing*). Ha, ha, ha . . . there's a girl! Well, I'll be back in half an hour. Goin' run up to the barber shop.

JOE. All right, Dad.

(*SOUND: Screen door slams.*)

JOE (*shaking his head*). I don't know how he's done it.

LEILA. Done what, Joe?

JOE. Stayed on in this one horse town for forty years.

LEILA. You don't like it here, Joe?

JOE. How can you ask such a question? Do *you* like Dalton?

LEILA. Well, I've never known any place else.

JOE. Leila . . . how much do you love me?

LEILA. More than anything else in the world, Joe.

JOE. What would you think of getting married now . . . and leaving Dalton!

LEILA. Leaving? . . . You mean . . . leave the *Banner?*

JOE. Yes.

LEILA. Joe, do you know what you're saying?

JOE. Look here! It's a telegram from the biggest paper in Chicago.

LEILA (*stunned*). Us . . . go to Chicago?

JOE. Yes, read it!

LEILA (*reading in a daze, picking out parts*). . . . Ten thousand dollars a year!

JOE. That's just to start.

LEILA. They want you to come up at once. But, Joe . . . your Dad!

JOE (*troubled*). I know,—but he—

LEILA. And you've got a wonderful opportunity right here!

JOE. Opportunity? Cramped up in a town so small it's practically confidential?

LEILA. Your father never felt that way.

JOE. Well, I do! I've demonstrated what I could do. This paper is making money now. I got advertising and collected for it. But I'm not going to do it the rest of my life.

LEILA. Joe, your father's dreamed and lived for the day when you'd carry on his work here.

JOE (*trying to reason*). Leila, the best the *Banner* could ever give us would be a modest living. I want to do *big* things.

LEILA. But this is *yours!* It's part of you. Why, your Dad feels that he and the *Banner* are as necessary in this town as the doctor and the minister. It's almost a mission in life.

JOE. That's Dad's idealism! . . . Oh, it's no use, Leila. I'm going where the money is.

LEILA. Your mind's made up?

JOE. Just about . . . if you'll go with me.

LEILA. Let me . . . let me think it over, will you, Joe?

JOE. The train for Chicago leaves at eight tonight.

LEILA. I'll let you know by then.

END OF ACT ONE

ACT II

(*SOUND: Newspaper press rumbling: steady click of papers being run off.*)

JEFF (*calling*). Mike! Hey, Mike!

MIKE (*older man*). What cha want, Jeff?

JEFF. Did you get that story about the paving on Fourth Street into the forms today?

MIKE. Yeah . . . it's in there.

JEFF. What cha think of it?

MIKE. You know me, Jeff . . . if you say it ain't right, there ain't nawthing good about it.

JEFF. Thanks, Mike.

MIKE. Say, Jeff . . . (*Confidentially*) . . . have ya heard anything 'bout the bank?

JEFF (*seriously*). Just a few rumours.

MIKE. Well . . . folks are sayin' a lot o' money's been stickin' to Tom Fulton's fingers, and the bank's nearly ready to fold up.

JEFF (*vehemently*). I don't believe a word of it! Tom Fulton ain't that stripe.

MIKE. Well, I been a little worried, Jeff. All my savings are in that bank.

JEFF. I'll go down there right after lunch and see Tom.

MIKE. Good.

(*SOUND: Door opening and closing, shutting off press sounds, press wire clicking.*)

JEFF. Well, she's rollin'. Anything comin' over the wires, Leila?

LEILA. No. Here they are. Usual things.

JEFF (*picking up bulletins*). Uuuuuummmmm. Yeah . . . drivel, most of it.

LEILA (*troubled*). Mr. Norris . . . has . . . has Joe said anything to you this morning?

JEFF (*reading*). Huh? . . . Said anything? . . . 'Bout what?

LEILA (*realizes he hasn't*). Oh! . . . Well, nothing . . . I'm going down to the bank to make a deposit.

JEFF. Say! . . . You been hearin' any talk about the bank, Leila?

LEILA. No, why?

JEFF. Oh, they're just rumours . . . never mind. Go ahead . . . make the deposit.

LEILA. See you later.

(*SOUND: Front door opens.*)

LEILA (*To Joe as he enters*). So long, Joe.

JOE (*calling back*). Bye!

(*SOUND: Front door slams closed.*)

JEFF. She's a great girl, that Leila. You're a lucky boy, Joe.

JOE (*uneasily*). I know.

JEFF. Don't know how I'll get along without her after you two get married.

JOE. Yes.

JEFF (*seriously*). What's on your mind, boy?

JOE. Oh . . . I was only thinking. Dad—why have you stayed on in a town like this all your life?

JEFF. I got a lot of friends.

JOE. Friends don't pay your bills.

JEFF. Well . . . I kinda feel I'm needed here. There's lots of plain people that have awful big thoughts sometimes and don't know how to put 'em into words. The good Lord sorta branded me with a knack for understandin' and sayin' what they can't say . . . so! I stick around.

JOE. But haven't you ever wanted to get away . . . move on to bigger things?

JEFF. No . . . when I move on . . . it'll be in a pine box.

JOE (*laughing affectionately*). Good old Dad! You don't have blood in your veins . . . it's printer's ink.

JEFF (*laughing, then suddenly*). Say! What started all this. You dissatisfied, Joe?

JOE (*hesitantly*). No, but . . . well, I've had an offer from another paper.

JEFF (*not taking it seriously*). Well, they've got their nerve. But then, I don't blame 'em for wantin' a good man.

JOE (*serious*). It's from the biggest paper in Chicago.

JEFF. Chicago, eh!

JOE. They've offered me . . . $10,000 a year.

JEFF (*whistling*). Boy, oh boy! (*Chuckling*) They really want you, don't they, Joe? . . . (*Then suddenly serious*) Say! . . . You mean you're thinking of going?

JOE. I didn't know how you might feel about it.

JEFF. *I'd* never stand in your way, Joe . . . that is, if you want to go. 'Course I'd always counted on you runnin' the *Banner* some day.

JOE. But if Leila and I get married, I could use a little more money.

JEFF. Sure . . . What does Leila think of this?

JOE. She's going to let me know tonight.

JEFF. Well, I want you to be happy, son. Whatever you decide is best for you . . . and Leila . . . is all right with me.

JOE. Gee, you're a brick, Dad. I knew you'd take it this way.

(*SOUND: Front door opens and slams.*)

BUTTONS. Hi, Boss! . . . Hello, Joe!

JEFF (*indulgently*). Well, well . . . it must be twelve o'clock.

BUTTONS. Sure is . . . and am *I* hungry!

JEFF. Well, how was school this morning?

BUTTONS. Rotten! . . . That teacher of mine, Miss Simpson . . . I hate her!

JEFF. Here, here . . . you know the Bible says you mustn't hate anyone, Buttons.

BUTTONS. Yeah, but the Bible was written before Miss Simpson was born.

JOE. I think it's about time we ate.

JEFF. Yes . . . let's go. C'mon, Buttons.

BUTTONS. Look! . . . Here comes Leila runnin' in the front door.

JEFF. Say, she's all outa breath.

LEILA (*excited*). Joe! Joe! Mr. Norris! . . . Hurry! There's a mob outside the bank!

JOE. A mob?

LEILA. Yes, there's more gathering every minute, and they're getting out of control.

JEFF. What are they doin'?

LEILA. They're liable to do anything! They're talking of lynching, tar and feathering . . . everything! I'm afraid something awful's going to happen!

JEFF. We've gotta get over there right away, Joe.

BUTTONS. I'm comin' too, Boss.

JEFF. No, you stay here.

BUTTONS. No sir. If you're goin', I'm goin'!

JEFF. All right . . . but stay close beside me.

(*SOUND: Door slams: Low, angry rumble of crowd voices is heard in distance. Volume slowly grows louder as if* JEFF, JOE, *etc. were getting closer.*)

MAN. He's tryin' to get outa town with our money!

VOICE. He's a crook!

VOICE. Let's storm the bank!

VOICE. We oughta lynch him!

VOICE. Hanging's too good fer him!

(*SOUND: Loud rumble of voices ad libbing threateningly, up strong: sudden crash of rock through bank window.*)

LEILA. Look! Someone's thrown a rock through the bank window!

JOE. Dad! I don't think you can do anything with this mob.

JEFF. Just wait! I know every person here! Let me through, Carl!

(*SOUND: Voices up again: then fade as:*)

JEFF (*calling out*). Just a minute, my friends, just a minute!

VOICE. It's Jeff Norris!

JEFF. Folks! I've heard the same rumours you have about what's goin' on here at the bank, an' I don't blame you for being worried, but listen . . . if there's anything wrong, this ain't the way to correct it!

VOICE. We're not goin' let Fulton get away!

JEFF. How do you know Fulton's done anything? How do you know he wants to get away? . . . This mob violence is a disgrace to Dalton. Why don't you give Fulton a chance to tell you the facts? Maybe things aren't as bad as you think they are!

VOICE. We want Fulton!

MOB (*shouting*). Yes! Lynch him! Hang him!

JEFF. I beg of you . . . go back to your homes and let the law deal with this!

BUTTONS. Boss . . . look out! There's a guy out there with a gun!

MOB (*shouting, bellowing*).

JOE. What are you going to do, Dad?

BUTTONS (*frantically*). Boss, Boss! . . . Look out . . . he's shooting!

(*SOUND: Revolver shot rings out:* MOB *suddenly is silent.*)

JOE. Buttons! . . . He jumped in front of Dad!

LEILA. He's been hit!

JEFF. Buttons! Buttons lad! Look here . . .

JOE (*shouting out*). Quiet! Quiet! Go get a doctor somebody . . . quick!

JEFF. Buttons lad . . . why, oh, why did you do it!

BUTTONS (*weakly*). Boss . . . I couldn't let 'em shoot you.

LEILA. How is he?

BUTTONS. I guess . . . I guess I won't get to be . . . a newspaper . . . man like you. . . .

JEFF. Yes you will, Buttons. You're goin' be all right.

BUTTONS. Gee . . . I wanted to be . . . like you . . . Boss.

JEFF. You're a better man than I ever was or could be, Buttons.

BUTTONS. You'll have to . . . get along without me, Boss. . . . (*Gasping*) So long. . . .

LEILA (*sobbing*). Oh ho hoh ho . . . Joe!

JOE. He's gone.

END OF ACT TWO

ACT III

(*SOUND: Motor car in background.*)

JOE (*wearily*). Gosh . . . what a night.

LEILA. What time is it . . . do you know, Joe?

JOE. Yes, it's . . . it's three o'clock.

LEILA. We've got to be back at the office in five hours. Look! . . . There's a light in the *Banner* office.

JOE (*stopping car*). Yeah.

LEILA. Who could be in there at this hour?

JOE. I don't know . . . unless it's . . . Dad.

LEILA. Yes . . . look! . . . Back there in his office!

(*SOUND: Clock in tower begins striking three.*)

LEILA. He's bending over his typewriter.

JOE (*thinking*). Yeah.

LEILA. Joe, I think we ought to go in and take him home.

JOE. He's been crushed by what happened today.

LEILA. Let's make him come with us.

JOE (*finally deciding*). No, I don't think so.

LEILA. But, Joe, he . . .

JOE (*thinking profoundly*). No, his heart and soul are choked. I doubt if he could say a word. But he can write! I remember when Mother died . . . he came down to the office and poured all the grief and beauty of humanity into that typewriter.

206

LEILA (*impressed*). Maybe you're right.

JOE. Yes . . . whatever he's writing, it's a masterpiece. He loved that kid . . . more than anyone will ever know; and Buttons idolized him. There's a bond between them now . . . that only God can touch.

LEILA. Shall we go?

JOE. Yes.

LEILA. Joe! You were supposed to leave for Chicago tonight.

JOE. Yes. It's strange how things happen sometimes, isn't it?

(*SOUND: Car starts up again.*)

(*SOUND: Car fades off: fade in church hymn at funeral service: this ends.*)

MINISTER. As we gather here to consecrate this little boy to His Heavenly Father, I should like to read as the service, an editorial that appeared in today's *Banner*. And because it expresses so tenderly the longing in our hearts and puts into words what is groping for expression from within each one of us, I want to read it: "Buttons was all the children of Dalton. He was all the children of the world. He loved little things and dreamed of things that were, to him, big . . ."

(*SOUND: Against background of* MINISTER *reading on ad lib.*)

LEILA. That's what your father was writing the other night, Joe.

JOE (*thinking*). Yes. The "big thoughts of plain people who don't know how to put 'em into words."

LEILA. When I read it, I wanted to cry. It said what I felt.

JOE. I guess it says what everybody feels. For the first time, I'm beginning to understand how he must feel about this job of his.

LEILA. It's more than . . . a job, Joe.

JOE (*slowly*). Yes, it is . . . more than . . . a job, Leila.

(*SOUND: Voice of* MINISTER *comes up.*)

MINISTER. Let us pray. O heavenly Father, we have today returned Buttons to Your house, remembering the words of Jesus who said: "In my Father's house are many mansions . . . I go to prepare a place for you." We know that he is now with You. And as we pray, we hear the echo of the Master's words; "This is my commandment. That ye love one another as I have loved you. Greater love hath no man than this, that a man lay down his life for his friend." Amen. (*Fade out.*)

(*FADE IN MUSIC: Appropriate type can break into this at any time, or pick up at finish.*)

(*SOUND: Typing.*)

FULTON. Hello, Leila.

LEILA. Oh, hello, Mr. Fulton.

FULTON. Jeff in?

LEILA. Yes . . . he's in his office. Go ahead in.

FULTON. Thanks.

(*SOUND: Footsteps. Swinging door.*)

FULTON. Hello, Jeff!

JEFF. Well! . . . Hello, Tom. Sit down.

FULTON. Thanks. I just thought you might be interested in hearing that they caught Barnes, that bank clerk.

JEFF. Got 'im, eh?

FULTON. Yes . . . they always do, Jeff.

JEFF. To think of what happened . . . just because he stole a thousand dollars!

FULTON. I think it's been a fearful lesson to every man in this town, Jeff.

JEFF. Yes. But at what price!

FULTON. Jeff, I've been thinking about that whole thing for the past two weeks. There's something I'd like to do.

JEFF. Yes?

FULTON. What you did that day was a credit to your profession.

And I'd like to endow a scholarship in Journalism at the University in your name.

JEFF (*thinking*). A scholarship in Journalism! That's a fine thing, Tom.

FULTON. I'm glad you approve.

JEFF. There's just one thing, Tom. Leave me out of it. Simply call it the "Buttons" scholarship, will you?

FULTON. If that's the way you want it.

JEFF. Fine.

FULTON. So long, Jeff. (*Fading out.*)

JEFF. 'Bye, Tom . . . 'Bye . . . Say, Leila!

LEILA (*coming up*). Yes, Mr. Norris?

JEFF. I haven't seen much of Joe for . . . well, the last couple of weeks. He's been kind of avoiding me.

LEILA. Oh, I'm sure he hasn't, Mr. Norris. He thought you'd prefer to be by yourself.

JEFF. Well, what I was wonderin' was . . . has he said any more to you about Chicago?

LEILA. No . . . he hasn't.

JEFF (*thinking*). Uuuuummmm.

LEILA. Have you said anything to him?

JEFF. No. I'll never influence him. He's gotta make up his own mind.

LEILA. Well, maybe if you'd . . .

JOE (*breaking in*). Am I intruding?

JEFF. No, no . . . why of course not, Joe.

JOE. Well, if you've got a few minutes, I'd like to talk to you a little.

JEFF. Sure, sure . . . come on, we'll go in here.

TELEGRAPH BOY. Telegram for Mr. Norris!

LEILA. I'll take it, Roy. (*Signing*) There you are!

JEFF. Was that for me, Leila?

LEILA. Yes! Here it is.

JEFF (*opening telegram*). I'll just take a second to read this . .
(*Stunned*) . . . to . . . to . . .

LEILA (*alarmed*). Mr. Norris! What's the matter?

JOE. Dad! What's happened?

JEFF (*hardly able to find words*). Joe! . . . this! . . . read this!

JOE. "Mr. Jefferson Norris: Your editorial in the *Dalton Banner*
entitled 'Buttons' has today been voted the Pulitzer Prize
for the most outstanding editorial of the year. (*Signed*) The
Pulitzer Prize Committee!" . . . Dad!

LEILA (*overjoyed*). Mr. Norris!

JEFF (*mumbling*). Me! . . . the Pulitzer Prize! . . .

JOE. It's what you've dreamed of, Dad!

LEILA. I can hardly believe it.

JEFF. Neither can I, Leila, neither can I.

JOE. They found you, Dad . . . out of everybody in the United
States!

JEFF (*almost to himself*). But it took Buttons.

LEILA. I think he's prouder than ever of you today, Mr. Norris.

JOE. I know he is. And Dad, I wanted to tell you that I wrote
Chicago today and told 'em I was sorry, but I had a permanent
job with the *Dalton Banner*.

JEFF (*overflowing*). You did that, Joe?

LEILA (*so grateful*). Oh, Joe!

JEFF (*almost fearfully*). Are you . . . sure of yourself, Joe?

JOE. I think I know something of how you must feel about this
job of yours now, Dad. Maybe it isn't glamorous, maybe it
doesn't pay well, maybe it's just a little tank-town newspaper,
but I've seen what you mean to these people . . . what they
mean to you. If I can be one tenth as good a newspaper man
as you are, I'll be proud to be a small town editor.

AFTER MIDNIGHT

By

JOHN KIRKPATRICK

CAST

MRS. WALLINGFORD
JANET
ANNABELLE
MRS. GRAVELY
MISS FISBEE
CHARLIE MICHAELS
ERNIE BISHOP

AFTER MIDNIGHT

(*MUSIC: The music should be of a somber, foreboding quality. Fade in for ten seconds and then under for background to* ANNOUNCER.)

ANNOUNCER. After Midnight.

(*MUSIC: Fade up for five seconds and then under to background.*)

ANNOUNCER. In the hours after midnight is told our story—the story of a dead woman! In the dead of the night we are in the old fashioned country home of Mrs. Wallingford. This house is a desolate one, miles from the nearest neighbor. It is a bleak and barren house and seems to mirror its lonely setting in the wind swept New England hills. The combination living room and dining room is in total darkness. The fire that was blazing in the large stone fireplace earlier in the evening has long since gone out. Outside the wind is blowing and lightning flashes. As the fitful illumination of the lightning comes through the windows the single rocking chair, an old worn one standing by the fireplace, appears in silhouette. For a moment all is silent. Then suddenly a stealthy step is heard upon the stairs—

(*SOUND: Fade in wind blowing in the distance. A burst of thunder. A door rattles. A light step is heard upon the stairs, coming down, and stopping. Then the step moves closer and again stops. Another step, this time more firm and forthright, descends the stairs. The door rattles again. The second pair of footsteps stops.*)

WALLINGFORD (*this voice of* MRS. WALLINGFORD, *the owner of the house, is deep, booming, contralto*). What's the matter?

JANET (*her voice is young, charming, but slightly strained at the moment*). Oh! (*She stifles a scream.*)

WALLINGFORD (*fades on mike. She is a stern but kindly old woman of seventy*). Ssh! You'll wake the whole house. You gallivantin' round down here in the dark! Turn on the lights.

(*SOUND: Click of a light switch.*)

WALLINGFORD. There! That's better. Let me look at you. What's the matter? You look pale. What made you get up?

JANET (*frightened*). I—I heard something.

WALLINGFORD. What?

JANET. That's just it. I don't know.

WALLINGFORD. Hm! Thought I heard somethin' too. But—well, don't reckon it was anything.

JANET. But it was! I heard it, too! Something—some sound—seems wrong somehow.

WALLINGFORD. It's just the wind. It's a wild night out. Better get back to bed. You'll catch your death o' cold, child. You're sick, you know—

JANET (*impatiently*). Oh, I'm not sick!

WALLINGFORD. Well, your stepfather said you were sick—

JANET. Because he wanted to get rid of me. Didn't want me home. Said I needed mountain air—ha!

WALLINGFORD. Maybe you do. Anybody'd think you didn't like it here. Mustn't hurt an old lady's feelin's, you know.

JANET (*gently*). Oh, I didn't mean *that,* Mrs. Wallingford. I—you've been awfully good to me and I—

(*SOUND: The door rattles again.*)

WALLINGFORD. What is it? What's the matter?

JANET. There! I heard it again! It's that door there—the door to Mrs. Duval's room! It's rattling. Hear it?

AFTER MIDNIGHT

WALLINGFORD. Hmm— Funny— If that door's rattlin' it means the window right 'cross from it's open—that window's north —where the wind is. Nobody but a fool would open that window on a night like this.

JANET (*in a whisper*). Oh, Mrs. Wallingford—I'm frightened!

WALLINGFORD. What you talkin' about?

JANET (*near hysteria*). I don't know—I don't know! All night long I—I've been hearing things in here!

WALLINGFORD. Hearing things?

JANET. Yes—yes! Noises—strange noises—a door being opened and shut—quietly—*too* quietly! And I heard whispering, too!

WALLINGFORD. Whispering? You must of dreamed it.

JANET. Oh, don't say that! I didn't! I know I didn't!

WALLINGFORD. Now, now, now. There, there. Ssh, ssh. I declare, child. You're just as nervy and jumpy as you can be.

JANET. I know, I know! I've been that way all evening! Ever since right after supper when those women started—

WALLINGFORD. Started what?

JANET. Oh, you know! Started fighting—fighting over who was to sit in that rocking chair near the fire. It was *awful!* Like cats baring their teeth! And it wasn't the first time! Why, you know yourself—

WALLINGFORD. Yes, yes, I know. But lemme tell you something, Janet—you don't mind if I call you "Janet," do you?

JANET. No, I like it.

WALLINGFORD. Well, then, lemme tell you something, Janet. Since I found the farm wouldn't pay an' been advertisin' for boarders to kind of help "eke out," as you might say, I've had some pretty queer customers. An' the ones I got now— well, I guess they ain't *much* worse'n some o' the others. (*Fades off mike*) Be back in a minute.

JANET. Where are you going?

WALLINGFORD. Goin' to put that window down. That poor fool in there must be blowed clean outer her bed by this time.

JANET. No—wait! Don't—please!

WALLINGFORD. Say! What's got into you?

JANET. Don't go! I mean—don't *you* go! Send for Charlie!

WALLINGFORD. Charlie? Think I need a State Policeman every time I want to shut a window in my house? "Charlie"—huh? When'd you get to callin' him "Charlie"?

JANET. Why—I—

WALLINGFORD. So you've fallen for the handsome Charlie, have you?

JANET (*confused*). Why, no—I—he—he's just been nice to me—that's all.

WALLINGFORD (*chuckling*). Well, I don't know as I blame you. If I had my hair back, 'n my teeth, 'n was fifty years younger, I don't know but I'd go after Charlie myself. Been meetin' him outside?

JANET. I—once or twice—yes.

WALLINGFORD. Hmm. Well, stir up the fire whilst I close that window. When I come back I'll fix us a little coffee.

(*SOUND: Footsteps. Door opens. The howling of the wind increases. The wind holds for a few seconds and over it we can hear* JANET *building a fire in the fireplace. Running footsteps of* MRS. WALLINGFORD *approach. The door slams shut violently.*)

WALLINGFORD (*out of breath, in horrified voice*). Good Lord!

JANET. What is it? What's the matter? Something's happened!

WALLINGFORD (*trying to control her voice*). G—get—Charlie!

JANET (*draws in her breath sharply*). Please, *please! What is it?*

WALLINGFORD (*breathing heavily*). Get—no, no—better—I— I'll do it!

AFTER MIDNIGHT

(*SOUND: Footsteps. Receiver of 'phone picked up. Bell crank turned and bell rings.*)

WALLINGFORD. I—I want—State Police— Yes— Quick!

JANET. W-what is it? *Please!*

(*SOUND: Footsteps coming coming down stairs. Stop abruptly.*)

WALLINGFORD. Annabelle! What you doin' up? Get back to bed!

ANNABELLE. But, I—I heard—

WALLINGFORD. Hush! Be quiet! Hello?—State Police?— Charlie?—Mrs. Wallingford, Charlie— Trouble up here— I want you to get up here quick— Quick, yes— You know I told you when you were here tonight things were, well, you know— Good Lord, Charlie, something awful. Better get hold of the Sheriff, Charlie, and—and Charlie—better get the Coroner, too!

(*SOUND: Receiver of 'phone is replaced on hook.*)

JANET. Coroner? Coroner? Then she—she—

WALLINGFORD (*in a hollow voice*) Mrs. Duval is—dead!

ANNABELLE (*screams loudly*). Ohhh!

(*MUSIC: Theme music comes up for five seconds and then fades out.*)

WALLINGFORD. Annabelle! Stop that moaning!

ANNABELLE (*moans*). Dead! Dead!

WALLINGFORD. Stop it, do you hear me! What are you doin' up? What woke you?

ANNABELLE. I—I *heard* things.

WALLINGFORD. And you got up to see what it was, huh?

ANNABELLE. No'm. No, ma'am.

WALLINGFORD. You're lying! You got more curiosity'n eighteen brass monkeys an' a car! What did you see?

ANNABELLE. Nothin'.

WALLINGFORD. *Answer my question! What did you see?*

ANNABELLE. I'm tellin' you, ain't I? I didn't see nothin'! I *couldn't* see nothin'! It was too dark!

(*SOUND: Timid footsteps come down stairs and stop.*)

GRAVELY (*she is about fifty. Her voice is the sweet, gushing, middle-aged variety. She is rather timid and very feminine*). Oh, what is it? What's the matter?

WALLINGFORD. So you're up, too, Mrs. Gravely? Sorry we woken you, but maybe it's just as well. Annabelle!

ANNABELLE. Yes'm?

WALLINGFORD. Go out in the kitchen and get the coffee perkin'. Go on now.

ANNABELLE. Yes'm.

(*SOUND: Footsteps retreating. Door opens and closes.*)

WALLINGFORD. Now, Mrs. Gravely, come on down. Take it easy there. Easy!

(*SOUND: Footsteps come down stairs.*)

FISBEE (*she is an old maid of forty. Her voice is hard, high, sharp staccato. Off mike*). What *is* the matter down there?

WALLINGFORD. Miss Fisbee? You up, too?

FISBEE. Who could sleep through all that din?

(*SOUND: Footsteps coming down stairs.*)

WALLINGFORD. Come down, Miss Fisbee. I want to talk to you— all of you.

FISBEE (*fading on mike*). For the heaven's sake! Move along, Mrs. Gravely!

GRAVELY. Oh, please! It's all I can do to—

FISBEE. Don't pamper yourself so! Now! What's happened? Who screamed?

WALLINGFORD. It was Annabelle screamed, Miss Fisbee. If you ladies'll jus' sit down, I'll—

FISBEE. I have no wish to sit down. What was that idiot screaming about? It sounded like Bedlam let loose!

WALLINGFORD. It's worse than Bedlam, Miss Fisbee. Will you sit down, please?

FISBEE. Why should I sit down? I'm cold! The place is like a barn! You might at least warm things us a little for us!

GRAVELY. Oh, dear! I was going to sit in that rocker!

FISBEE. Were you?

GRAVELY. Oh, please, Miss Fisbee! I'm so cold! I'm shivering!

FISBEE. Well, stop shivering—and you won't be so cold.

GRAVELY. But you just said you didn't want to sit down and—Oh, my heart—my heart!

JANET. Here, Mrs. Gravely! Sit here!

GRAVELY. Thank you, Janet, my dear. Oh, dear, my heart!

FISBEE. There's nothing wrong with her heart! She just uses it to get what she wants!

GRAVELY. Don't you *dare* say a thing like that!

WALLINGFORD. Oh, stop it, you two!

GRAVELY. I never get the rocking chair. She's always in it—always!

FISBEE. *I'm* always in it? You mean *Mrs. Duval's* always in it!

JANET. Don't say that! Don't speak of Mrs. Duval like that when she—

WALLINGFORD. Wait, Janet!

FISBEE. Why *shouldn't* I speak of Mrs. Duval like that? She always makes a bee line for this chair the moment she comes in the room. And she knows—because I've told her a dozen times—that this is my chair! *My* chair! I *like* this chair! I like to sit in this chair close to the fire and—dream! (*Her voice trails off.*)

WALLINGFORD. Well, I don't think you'll be bothered with Mrs. Duval any more.

GRAVELY. You mean she's leaving? Oh, I'm glad, I'm glad!

WALLINGFORD (*sternly*). Mrs. Gravely!

GRAVELY. I can't help it! I hate her—I *hate* her!

WALLINGFORD. *Wait!*

GRAVELY. I won't wait! She's been cruel to me—cruel, I tell you! She knows I've a bad heart—and she's always doing things to frighten me—to torment me!

WALLINGFORD. *Stop it!* Get hold of yourself! Listen to me! I'm 'fraid it's gonna be a shock but—well, there's been a—an accident—'n Mrs. Duval's—dead.

GRAVELY. Dead?

WALLINGFORD. Yes.

GRAVELY. In that room there?

WALLINGFORD. An' that ain't all neither.

JANET. What do you mean?

GRAVELY. Dead! (*Whispers, her voice full of horror*) I don't like— Oh, I want to— I *must* go away!

WALLINGFORD. Sit still, Mrs. Gravely! Well, Miss Fisbee, did you hear what I said?

FISBEE (*speaks automatically, in a dream*). What? Oh, yes— yes— You said someone was dead—

WALLINGFORD. Mrs. Duval.

FISBEE (*slowly*). Oh, well—I *told* her this was my chair. *Now* maybe she knows it!

JANET (*horrified*). Oh, how *can*—!

WALLINGFORD. Do you know what you're saying, Miss Fisbee?

FISBEE. Perfectly well—yes.

WALLINGFORD. Maybe this'll shake you! I said that wasn't all— her just bein' dead—and it ain't! Mrs. Duval—was *murdered!*

JANET (*gasping*). No—no—

WALLINGFORD. *Yes!* Murdered!

GRAVELY. In—in there? Right in that room?

WALLINGFORD. Yes. In there—on the floor—lying in a pool of blood—with a—with a *knife* driven through her heart!

220

AFTER MIDNIGHT

(*MUSIC: Fades in with a climax. Up for ten seconds and then fades out.*)

(*SOUND: Three loud knocks on heavy door. Footsteps. Door opens. Wind increases.*)

WALLINGFORD. Hello, Charlie.

CHARLIE (*deep, pleasing voice, about thirty-five*). 'Lo, Mrs. Wallingford! What's the trouble? Evenin', ladies. Mornin', rather. This is Ernie, Mrs. Wallingford. Ernie Bishop. New on the force, don't think you know him.

WALLINGFORD. Good evenin', Ernie.

(*SOUND: Door closes.*)

ERNIE. Pleased to know you. (*He has a young voice, rather shy.*)

CHARLIE. Well, Mrs. Wallingford?

WALLINGFORD. In there, Charlie—Mrs. Duval!

CHARLIE (*whistles*). Whew! And to think—we was all sittin' 'round that table havin' coffee together at nine o'clock—just before I went on duty. Are you sure she's—

WALLINGFORD. She's cold, Charlie, stone cold. And there's a knife sticking in her heart.

ERNIE. A knife stickin'— Gosh! That's—that's—

CHARLIE. Take it easy, Ernie. Like I said—Ernie's—well, new —not used to—you know. But he's O.K., Mrs. Wallingford, and—well, might as well get it over with.

ERNIE. Want me to go with you, Charlie?

CHARLIE. No, kid, never mind. No use of both of us goin' in. I guess it ain't a very pretty sight.

WALLINGFORD. No, it ain't.

CHARLIE. You stay out here, Ernie. Sort of keep an eye on things while I— I got the Sheriff and the Coroner, Mrs. Wallingford. They'll be over soon's they can get here. You take care of the ladies, Ernie. You know your stuff—names, addresses, when they last saw the deceased—all that.

ERNIE. What about *outside,* Charlie. Want me to look?

CHARLIE. For gosh sakes, you think a guy would walk in, commit murder, and then stick around for somebody to nab him?

ERNIE. But there might be clues—you know, footprints and—well, clues. Suppose I take a look with my flashlight.

CHARLIE (*hurriedly*). No, no use! Ground's hard as a rock. Been frozen for three days. You stay here and do as I told you.

ERNIE. Okay.

(*SOUND: Footsteps retreat. Door opens and closes.*)

ERNIE. Now, ladies, you heard what Char—what the senior patrolman said. Any information is welcome and—well—(*Tries to be very businesslike*) First, names and addresses. I—I'll begin with you, ma'am. Er—if—if you don't mind.

JANET. Of course not. Janet Browder. 416 Hickswood Street. Philadelphia.

ERNIE. Thanks. Now, did you know the deceased? By the way, you say she was Mrs. Duval?

WALLINGFORD. Yes, Primrose Duval.

ERNIE. Gosh! Pretty name!

FISBEE. A little too good to be true.

ERNIE. What's that, ma'am?

FISBEE. Oh, don't be a fool, Officer! Nobody was ever named "Primrose Duval"!

ERNIE. I see. And how well did *you* know her, Mrs.—er—

FISBEE. *Miss*—Ellen Fisbee.

ERNIE. And your address?

WALLINGFORD. 'Scuse me, Officer Bishop, but hadn't you better finish with Janet—Miss Browder, there before you go on to another?

ERNIE. Yes, sure. Er—now, Miss Browder, did you know the—

222

JANET. No, I didn't. I mean, not before I came here two weeks ago. I—I didn't like her.

ERNIE. Well, I—I wouldn't say that if I were you. I mean, you don't have to come out with a statement like that—

JANET. But it's quite true. I know she's—dead—and all that, but I can't help it. I didn't like her.

WALLINGFORD. None of us "liked" her, Officer. She wasn't the kind. I don't believe she even *wanted* to be liked. But Janet got on with her's well as anybody.

ERNIE (*relieved*). Then—that's all right, then.

WALLINGFORD. No, it ain't all right! The truth ain't never gonna hurt anybody, an' it's got to come out! Janet, are *you* gonna tell him about las' night—or me?

JANET. I couldn't understand it at all.

ERNIE. Understand what?

JANET. The way—Mrs. Duval—*looked* at me. It was—oh, I didn't think anybody else saw it—but it was horrible—*horrible!* It frightened me so that—that—

WALLINGFORD. Didn't you speak to Charlie about it?

JANET. Yes. I was terrified. So when he was taking the soiled cups out to the kitchen last night, I picked up some more cups and followed him.

ERNIE. What did he say?

JANET. Oh, he made light of it—or tried to! But I know—I *know* he was only trying to keep me from being afraid!

ERNIE. I see. Now, Miss Fisbee. First, your address, please.

FISBEE. I—I live with my nephew—or *did*.

ERNIE. And his address?

FISBEE. I shan't give it to you! I didn't know the so-called "Primrose Duval" until she arived here about a month ago— for what reason I can't possibly imagine.

ERNIE. And just what do you mean by that last?

FISBEE. I mean that she didn't belong here. I don't belong here, either, of course, but well—that's different. And anyway, here I am. Officer, Mrs. Wallingford has my nephew's address —he sends her the checks for my board. I'm going to my room.

ERNIE (*firmly*). No. You're going to stay here.

FISBEE. Oh, very well. (*Pause*) My chair, please, Mrs. Gravely.

GRAVELY. I have it now. And it isn't your chair. It belongs to the house.

FISBEE. *My chair, please!*

GRAVELY. Officer! She's already murdered one woman tonight because of this chair. Are you going to stand by and see me murdered too?

JANET. Don't, don't! Please, Officer, can't you make them stop?

ERNIE. Wait a minute! Sit down over here, please, Miss Fisbee.

FISBEE. Why should I?

ERNIE. Because I say so! (*Pause*) Thank you. Now, you say Mrs. Duval didn't belong here. Just what—

FISBEE (*impatiently*). Oh, the woman was bored. She had no resources—within herself, I mean. She didn't like long walks, animals, dogs, cows, chickens—anything about the country. She couldn't bear to read anything except trash. She belonged in the city.

ERNIE. Then what made her come here?

FISBEE. I neither know nor care.

ERNIE. I see. And when did you last see her, Miss Fisbee?

FISBEE. Just before I went to my room—about eight-thirty, I should say.

ERNIE. Thank you. Now, Mrs.—er—Gravely, is it?

GRAVELY. Mrs. Charles Gordon Gravely. I live at 40 Selma Road, in Grace Gardens—just outside of Newark. My son is a lawyer —a very prominent lawyer in—

ERNIE (*quickly*). Yes, I see. And now, Mrs. Gravely, about Mrs. Duval? From what you said a while ago, I sort of gathered that you thought the same as Miss Fisbee. That Mrs. Duval was not her real name.

GRAVELY. I never saw her until she came here—but there was nothing very "real" about Mrs. Duval—except—

ERNIE. Except?

GRAVELY. Oh, ask somebody else, please! I don't know what! I don't want to be rude but, you see, Officer, I—well, I don't know whether I'm psychic or not—but all the time Mrs. Duval was here I seemed to get the strangest feeling—of some secret undercurrent—some mystery—

WALLINGFORD. *Wait!*

GRAVELY. Oh! What is it? I'm frightened!

WALLINGFORD. You've got cause to be frightened. We all have!

ERNIE. What do you mean, Mrs. Wallingford?

WALLINGFORD. I mean—if you can kill *once,* you can kill again —to hide the first killin'! Look! All of you! I want you to cast your eyes 'round this room—an' see what's missin'.

FISBEE. A knife—that's usually here on this table—a paper-knife.

WALLINGFORD (*grimly*). Yeah. I know where the knife is—but—

JANET. Wait, wait! Something else is gone. The vase! The Chinese vase! It always stood on that table there!

WALLINGFORD. Right! Soon's I came in this room this mornin', I knew some'n was wrong. But it was only jus' now I figured it out.

ERNIE. A vase, you say?

JANET. Yes, a Chinese one.

ERNIE. Why should anybody steal it?

WALLINGFORD. I didn't say it was—stolen, did I? I said it wasn't there, and it ain't.

FISBEE. Perhaps somebody broke it! Who cares?

JANET. But then—then where are the pieces?

WALLINGFORD. Funny—that's jus' what I was wonderin' about myself. It was here las' night when I went to bed! If it was broke—it was broke in the middle of the night! An' by somebody who took the trouble to pick up the pieces and hide 'em so's I wouldn't find out about it! (*Calls*) Annabelle!

ANNABELLE. Yes'm?

WALLINGFORD. You broke that vase!

ANNABELLE. Oh! No'm! I didn't, I didn't!

WALLINGFORD. You did! You was down here las' night! Down here in this room! What did you see?

ANNABELLE. I *tole* you I didn't see nothin'. I *couldn't* see nothin'!

WALLINGFORD. But you *heard* some'n!

ANNABELLE (*terrified*). Yes'm, yes'm! But I—I—it was jus' whisperin'—like I told you. An' I couldn't hear good, so I started sneakin' down the stairs—an' then I heard a door close—an' I eased all the way down— It wuz dark—an' I couldn't see nothin'—an' I—I bumped inter that table an'—an' the vase fell over—

WALLINGFORD. With a crash?

ANNABELLE. Yes'm. I made such a noise I got scairt—an' hid back o' them curtains there—an' I waited an' waited an' kep' on waitin' an'—then I didn't hear nothin'—so I crep' out again. An' lit a match—an' picked up the pieces—an' went upstairs.

WALLINGFORD. Think, now—think! Did you hear anything—else?

ANNABELLE. Yes'm, but I—I didn't know what it wuz then!

WALLINGFORD. What did you hear?

ANNABELLE. Once—jus' 'fore the vase fell over—I heard—a sorter moan—like somebody wuz tryin' to cry out an' couldn't!

GRAVELY. I can't stand it! (*Screams*) Ohhh!

AFTER MIDNIGHT

(*SOUND: Door opens and closes suddenly.*)

JANET (*screams*). Ohh! (*Relieved*) Oh, Charlie! You scared us so!

CHARLIE. What? Oh—gee—gosh—I—I'm sorry. Gosh, what a fool I was to—

WALLINGFORD. 'S all right, Charlie. We just wasn't lookin' for you to come in by the front door. We thought you'd come out o' *her* door.

CHARLIE. Oh—well, I thought I'd take a look around to satisfy Ernie. Climbed out the window to see if I could find any traces—outside.

WALLINGFORD. An' did you find any?

CHARLIE (*pause imperceptibly*). Not a one. What's going on here?

WALLINGFORD. Annabelle. She was down here las' night. She was in this room while—well, at the very minute Mrs. Duval was killed.

CHARLIE (*whistles*). Whew! Umm— What'd she see—or hear?

WALLINGFORD. She heard the poor woman try to—cry out.

CHARLIE. Anything else?

ANNABELLE. Naw! An' I ain't sayin' nothin' more! I don't care what you do to me—put me in jail if you want to—anything! I ain't sayin' nothin' more to nobody!

(*SOUND: Footsteps running up stairs.*)

(*MUSIC: Up for five seconds and then fade under and out.*)

WALLINGFORD. Well, Charlie, now that they're all in the kitchen having coffee, what are we going to do?

CHARLIE. I don't know, Mrs. Wallingford. Say, did you tell Ernie about—well, what you told me last night?

WALLINGFORD. I didn't need to. He saw it himself.

ERNIE. Saw what?

WALLINGFORD. Those women—how they hate each other.

227

ERNIE. Gosh, yes. And did they hate Mrs. Duval that way, too?

WALLINGFORD. I'm 'fraid so.

ERNIE. But why? I mean, why do they hate each other so?

WALLINGFORD. 'Cause they ain't got much else to do—but hate! They all say as how Mrs. Duval didn't belong here! None of 'em do!

ERNIE. Then why are they here?

WALLINGFORD. 'Cause they ain't wanted at home! They're all dependent on somebody else—an' it's easier an' cheaper for that "somebody else" to keep 'em here with me! With Miss Fisbee, it's her nephew. With Janet, it's her stepfather—an' her mother mus' be a fool to allow it! With Mrs. Gravely, poor woman, it's her own son!

ERNIE. And—Mrs. Duval?

WALLINGFORD. She was—different. Yet I suppose she wasn't wanted neither. Suppose that's why she was murdered.

CHARLIE. That's why most people get murdered, ain't it?

WALLINGFORD. Charlie—you think one of those—women out there in the kitchen killed Mrs. Duval?

CHARLIE. Not Janet!

WALLINGFORD. No, not Janet. An' Annabelle—well, she'd lie an' steal, maybe—but I don' b'lieve she's got the nerve to stick a knife into anybody. But the others—?

CHARLIE (*kindly*). I hate to say it, Mrs. Wallingford, but, hang it all! You know how they fought with Mrs. Duval—both of 'em. You told me last night things were getting so bad you were worried—

WALLINGFORD. I know—I know—

CHARLIE. The three of 'em cooped up here—bad weather so they couldn't get out—you know how women—men, too, for that matter—can get on each other's nerves—how little things can get to look like mighty big ones—especially when—well, Mrs.

228

Gravely and Miss Fisbee—neither one of 'em's what you might call "normal."

WALLINGFORD. I know, I know— But the front door, Charlie— the front door!

CHARLIE. Front door? What about it?

WALLINGFORD. I told you! It was unlocked! An' the window— the window to Mrs. Duval's room—it was wide open with the wind blowin' in!

CHARLIE. Fake stuff! To pull the wool over our eyes and make us think it was an outsider!

WALLINGFORD. But why—why *both* of 'em, Charlie? The window *an'* the door?

CHARLIE. Right! You've got it there, Mrs. Wallingford! *You* answer me that question! Why *both* of 'em? If the murderer came in the window why didn't he go out the window? If he came in the front door, why didn't he go out that way? Besides, you locked the door on the inside—and the key was in it. And the window *must* of been locked on the inside when Mrs. Duval went to bed.

ERNIE. Why?

CHARLIE. Because nobody would have gone to bed on a night like this with it open—an it *won't stay down unless it's locked!* It's broken or something. No, whoever killed Mrs. Duval came from inside and was doin' all she could—too much, in fact—to make it look the other way!

ERNIE. But, wait! It might have been an outsider—someone she knew and unlocked the door for!

CHARLIE. She didn't know anybody 'round this neck of the woods.

WALLINGFORD. How do you know she didn't?

CHARLIE. I don't know. But did she?

WALLINGFORD. That's just it. I'm as ignorant as you are.

ERNIE. Didn't she get any letters?

WALLINGFORD. None. None at all.

ERNIE. But—her board. How'd she pay that?

WALLINGFORD. Cash—always cash.

ERNIE. But where'd she get the cash?

CHARLIE. Oh, she's only been here four weeks. She might have brought that much with her.

ERNIE. Then gee-whilligens! Gosh! Maybe she's got more cash! And maybe that's why she was murdered!

WALLINGFORD. She always kep' her trunk locked—if that's any help.

CHARLIE. There's no cash in her trunk. Found the key in her hand-bag. 'Course I didn't make a complete search—just a once over.

ERNIE. Any papers—things like that?

CHARLIE. Nope. Nothing—

WALLINGFORD. Strange, ain't it? I can't help worryin' 'bout that window. The window *an'* the door. And then—some other things—

CHARLIE. What other things?

WALLINGFORD. Oh, the strange feelin' Mrs. Gravely got—the whisperin' Annabelle heard— Then there was the broken vase—an' most of all—what Mrs. Duval did today.

CHARLIE. What did she do today?

WALLINGFORD. She went out—for a walk.

ERNIE. Gosh—nothing so strange about that, is there?

WALLINGFORD. Not for mos' people—but for Mrs. Duval—yeah. She hated walkin'. She'd do anythin' to keep from walkin'. But yesterday she walked—went out right after Janet did— Charlie, Janet says she told you 'bout it an'—

CHARLIE. Yeah, yeah. But still I don't see anything so—

(*SOUND: Door opens suddenly.*)

JANET. Excuse me for interrupting, but—well, I've been in the kitchen puzzling my brain over why Mrs. Duval was staying here.

CHARLIE. You're not interrupting, Janet. Well—?

JANET. I wondered— Miss Fisbee thought Mrs. Duval was a thief. That she worked in a department store and stole things —cheap jewelry, silks, lingerie, things like that—

ERNIE. How about it, Charlie? See anything like that in her trunk?

CHARLIE. Plenty of it, lots of it, yes. 'Course we don't know if it was stolen but—

JANET. But if they were—wouldn't that explain why she was here? That they'd found out about it—and reported it—and that she was trying to get away from the police?

WALLINGFORD (*softly*). Oh, good Lord!

EVERYBODY (*ad lib*). What is it? What's the matter? You sick? (etc. etc.)

WALLINGFORD. No, no, no—wait! Wait 'til I get my breath! It—it jus' hit me—that's all.

JANET. What hit you?

WALLINGFORD. The truth!

ERNIE. You mean you know—

WALLINGFORD. I mean I know all about it—an' I wish I didn't!

CHARLIE. Steady, old girl! What is it?

WALLINGFORD. Oh, Charlie, you was right! I wouldn't believe it! I didn't want to b'lieve it! But you was right!

ERNIE. About Mrs. Gravely—and Miss Fisbee?

JANET. You mean—one of them—did—murder? No, no! It *can't* be! It isn't *true!*

WALLINGFORD. Guess you boys'd like to make the arrest, wouldn't you?

ERNIE. Gee, gosh, yes!

CHARLIE. Sure, but—

WALLINGFORD (*sharply*). Then do as I say.

ERNIE. But—but, gosh, Mrs. Wallingford, we—we don't know which one it is.

WALLINGFORD. *I* do.

CHARLIE. How?

WALLINGFORD. Something Annabelle said. Now, Charlie! We got to move, an' move in a hurry! I don't want no more murders in my house tonight.

ERNIE. Gosh! Annabelle? But she's out there with 'em now! If she knows which one did it—

WALLINGFORD. Annabelle knows—but she doesn't know she knows. Till she does she's safe. Janet, go out in the kitchen an' call 'em in. Tell 'em—tell 'em Officer Michaels wants 'em.

JANET. All right, Mrs. Wallingford.

(*SOUND: Footsteps and door closes.*)

CHARLIE. Say, what is this—a trap?

WALLINGFORD. Yeah—an' *I* got to spring it. Ernie, when they get in here, I want you to slip out. At the bottom o' the cellar stairs you'll find a fuse box. Take it out.

ERNIE. Take it out? You mean—just unscrew it, don't you?

WALLINGFORD. No! I mean take it out, lose it, throw it away— so the lights can't come on. It's got to be dark a long, long time for me to do what I got to do.

CHARLIE. What is it you got to do?

WALLINGFORD. Scare the livin' daylights out o' Annabelle—so she'll say what she knows—an' don't know she knows. An', Ernie, right now—'fore they get here—gimme your gun!

ERNIE. Give you—my gun?

WALLINGFORD. That's what I said.

ERNIE. Oh, but *say!* Gee, gosh, Mrs. Wallingford, I can't do *that!*

It's against regulations. Anyway, Charlie'll be here—he'll have his gun.

WALLINGFORD. Charlie won't be here.

CHARLIE. What's that?

WALLINGFORD. Charlie'll be outside. Right outside the door there —so nobody can slip by in the dark.

CHARLIE. You're the boss. But, say, let *one* of us stay here. I—I'm scared for *you,* old girl.

WALLINGFORD. No, Charlie—much obliged but— Quick—'fore they get here. You seat 'em, Charlie, but I'll tell you where to put 'em. I want Janet over here against the wall. Miss Fisbee there by the table. Mrs. Gravely in the rocker by the fire. An' Annabelle in that chair between the table and the door.

CHARLIE. O.K., I got it. An' where'll you be?

WALLINGFORD. Over here—here at the foot of the stairs—where I can hide this—this gun o' yours, Ernie.

(*MUSIC: Comes up for five seconds and then fades under and out.*)

JANET. Where's Charlie?

WALLINGFORD. He—he's gone.

FISBEE. Ssh! Ssh! Please. Mrs. Wallingford is going to favor us with one of her delightful little stories. Or perhaps a whole speech—since she seems to be writing it out.

WALLINGFORD. No, Miss Fisbee, it ain't a speech. It's a *list*—for you, Ernie.

ERNIE. A list—for me?

WALLINGFORD. Yeah, the one you asked for. Remember? Better read it—when you go—where you're going.

ERNIE (*catching on*). Oh, yes. Sure. Er—much obliged. Well, so long.

(*SOUND: Footsteps. Door opens and closes.*)

233

FISBEE. Why are you sending those policemen away—one out one door and one out the other?

WALLINGFORD. 'Cause I got a little story to tell you—

FISBEE. I don't wish to hear a story. I want those policemen back here.

WALLINGFORD. The story of Mrs. Duval—

FISBEE. I'm not interested. I want those men summoned at once!

GRAVELY. Oh! What is it? What is it?

FISBEE. There's some trickery going on here. I don't know just what but—

WALLINGFORD. Get back where you belong, both of you! The—story—of—a—dead woman!

FISBEE. Of a dead woman? You mean of a live one, don't you?

WALLINGFORD. What's that?

FISBEE. I think *you* murdered Mrs. Duval!

JANET. No! No!

WALLINGFORD (*laughs harshly*). Me murdered Mrs. Duval? Well, I'll tell you a secret—maybe I did! Anyway, we're gonna find out! Annabelle! Annabelle, it's your last chance! I want the truth about what you heard when—

(SOUND: *Click of light switch.*)

JANET (*screams*). Ohhh!

GRAVELY. The lights! The lights! What's happened to the lights?

WALLINGFORD. Something's happened. Fuse blew out, I guess, must of—

ANNABELLE. Turn on them lights! Oh, oh Lord save us!

JANET. Charlie—Charlie! Where's Charlie!

EVERYBODY (*ad lib*). Help!—Get away!—Who's this?—The lights! (*Pandemonium.*)

ANNABELLE (*screams suddenly, ending in a choked, rasping sound*).

234

AFTER MIDNIGHT

(*SOUND: Click of light switch.*)

JANET. Oh, thank heavens, the lights are on again! Charlie! Charlie, what are you doing?

WALLINGFORD. All right, let her go, Charlie—an' put your hands up!

CHARLIE. What do you think you're doing?

JANET. Charlie! Charlie!

WALLINGFORD. I know what I'm doing! Put your hands up, I said! (*Calls*) Ernie! Ernie!

CHARLIE. You won't get away with this kind of stuff!

GRAVELY. Oh, what is it?

WALLINGFORD. Stay where you are, Charlie! An put 'em up. If you don't—so help me, I'll blow the top o' your head off!

CHARLIE. You will like fun! I—

JANET. No, no—Charlie! Don't shoot, Charlie!

CHARLIE. Let go of me, Janet! Let go of me!

JANET. No, no! What are you doing?

CHARLIE. Let go of my arm, Janet!

WALLINGFORD. Move, Janet! Get out of the way! I'm gonna shoot!

CHARLIE. Let go, Janet! You'll get hurt!

JANET. No, no! I won't move!

WALLINGFORD. Then make him drop that gun! He's already killed one woman, tried to kill another. And he ain't gonna—

(*SOUND: Gun explodes.*)

JANET. Charlie! Charlie!

WALLINGFORD. I mean business, Charlie. So if you don't want her hit—

CHARLIE. All right, all right. Don't shoot! Here's my gun.

(*SOUND: Gun drops on floor.*)

ERNIE. What's going on here? Gosh! Charlie!

WALLINGFORD. Put your hands up, Charlie. Ernie.

ERNIE. Right here, ma'am!

WALLINGFORD. Pick up his gun, Ernie! Keep it turned on him.

CHARLIE. Oh, you needn't worry now. I won't try anything.

ERNIE. But I—gee—gosh! I—I don't get all this.

CHARLIE (*quietly*). Some of it I don't get either—about the fuse.

WALLINGFORD. Oh, I just told Ernie not to take the fuse out. But knowin' you'd be listenin' I wrote it on a piece of paper. *I* turned the lights out here at this switch.

JANET. Oh, I—I can't believe it! I—oh! (*Starts to cry.*)

ERNIE. Me neither. I don't understand why—how—

WALLINGFORD (*wearily*). Never mind, Ernie. It's a long story, I guess. Ain't it, Charlie?

CHARLIE. Not so long. I married her—then I found out she was a—a thief! I tried but I couldn't break her. Sent her up. I tried to get out from under. Moved to this state. Got on the State Police. Everythin' was goin' fine, but— Well, she traced me and came here. I gave her the money for the board, of course, but we—we hated each other. Said she had to see me last night. She let me in but—I was ready for her. I—I'd seen the—the knife there. Picked it up on my way in. But then, after I'd—done it—there was a crash in here. I was scared so I beat it out the window. That was why——

WALLINGFORD. Yes—the door *an'* the window.

ERNIE. Sheriff's pulling in the driveway.

CHARLIE. Yeah, I'm comin', only—I'd like to know—'course I can see now Annabelle was just a plant—she didn't know anything. But how'd you happen to spot me, Mrs. Wallingford?

WALLINGFORD. It was like a fire—just waiting for a match. The match was one little word—the word, "police."

CHARLIE. I don't get you.

WALLINGFORD. Oh, I guess my poor old brain was gettin' ready to take in something only it didn't seem to do it. You not takin' Ernie with you when you went in to search—your climbin' out the window an' comin' back in here through the front door—lookin' to havin' a reason for your footprints —if there was any. Then you made the real slip.

CHARLIE. What was that?

WALLINGFORD. Least I made the slip—an' you let it go. Janet said she'd told you about the way Mrs. Duval had looked at her. Later when I was tellin' you 'bout Mrs. Duval goin' out yesterday, I got mixed up and said "Janet said she told you about it" and you said, "Yeah, I know, I know"—

CHARLIE. Well—?

WALLINGFORD. But Janet couldn't of told you 'cause she didn't know. It was Janet Mrs. Duval followed and Janet didn't know until Annabelle spilled the beans. So it must have been Mrs. Duval herself who told you that.

CHARLIE. Yeah, she told me. She was jealous an' she followed Janet when Janet met me yesterday.

WALLINGFORD. Then just a little while ago Janet said she wondered if Mrs. Duval *was* a thief and that maybe she was tryin' to get away from the *police*. I happened to be lookin' right at *you* then an'—well, somethin' clicked. I *knew*. She wasn't here to get away from the police—it was to get *to* 'em, at least, to one of 'em.

JANET. Charlie! I didn't mean—

CHARLIE. I know you didn't suspect—but it's better this way— better it turned out just like it did.

JANET. No, no, I don't believe it, I can't believe it! Even now— oh, say you didn't—

CHARLIE. No, I did it all right. But don't feel sorry about anything. Just—just forget.

JANET. Forget?

CHARLIE. Oh, you will someday, when it's all over. Some day, I hope—there'll be—someone else—some other guy—a younger guy—with nothing out of the past to—to mess it up. Meantime—well—it's better this way.

WALLINGFORD. I'm sorry, Charlie.

CHARLIE (*kindly*). It's been tough on you, old girl.

WALLINGFORD. Life's just naturally been tough on me.

CHARLIE. I know. But listen—even if Janet hadn't got in my way—I don't believe I'd have—hurt *you*.

WALLINGFORD. No—I don't believe you would of, Charlie.

CHARLIE. And you—you'll see to it that—she's happy, won't you? You'll keep her here with you and—all that?

WALLINGFORD. Sure—sure I will, Charlie.

CHARLIE. Well, then—guess that's about all there is to say, ain't it? Come on, Ernie, let's go.

(*SOUND: Footsteps. Door opens and closes.*)

JANET. No—no—no! He can't go like that! He can't! He can't!

WALLINGFORD (*quietly and gently*). Ssh! Ssh! You musn't, child, you musn't! Didn't you hear what he said? It's better this way.

JANET (*sobs quietly*).

(*MUSIC: Fades in and up.*)

A PENNY SAVED

By

DENA REED

CAST

PENELOPE BROWNELL
PETER BROWNELL
MR. BARKINS
SODA FOUNTAIN BOY
TAXI DRIVER
JIMMY JENKINS

A PENNY SAVED

ANNOUNCER. Without so much as a "pardon-me" to the people she bumped and jostled while dashing across the great waiting room of Grand Central Station, red-headed Penelope Brownell swept from the train gate as the local commuter's special pulled in . . . ran down the stairs of the subway entrance, and just managed to squeeze through the door of the express headed for Wall Street. Eleven minutes later she rushed through the ante-room of her uncle's brokerage office—

(*SOUND: Running footsteps—office background lightly. Mike stays with footsteps ending in fast door opening and closing. Background cuts.*)

PENNY (*slightly out of breath*).—Whew—made it. Ten minutes past three . . . on the dot.

UNC. Well, well, Penny, my dear. I wasn't expecting you.

PENNY. Hello, Unc, how's the market?

UNC. Huh. Don't trouble your pretty head about that. I'll be ready to go home in five minutes, kitten, so I'll drive back with you.

PENNY. No! No! Uncle Pete, I came to have a *business* talk with you.

UNC (*sighing*). Okay. How much?

PENNY. Unc, you pain me. Have I ever overstepped my allowance?

Unc. No. Can't say that you have. What's up?

Penny. Instead of being a liability, your niece, Penelope, is about to blossom forth as an asset.

Unc. She always was an asset as far as I'm concerned.

Penny. Ooh, nice. Here's a kiss for that. What I'm trying to say is that you're going to give me a job.

Unc. I'm going to— Look here, Penny, you think up the darndest things to waste my time. Now that you've graduated from college, your job is to get yourself a husband and babies. I want something besides gout to think about in my old age.

Penny. Oh, so I'm supposed to marry just so you can have more nieces and nephews to bully.

Unc. And I flattered myself I treated you pretty well.

Penny. Oh, you do, darling. Too well. But that's just my point, you're entitled to some return on your investment.

Unc. What investment? What are you talking about?

Penny. Raising me in the way to which I was *un*accustomed. You know, Unc, you may not realize it, but I've turned out to be quite a luxury.

Unc. I guess I can afford it.

Penny. Oh but *I* can't. I mean—it isn't fair of you to make me give you a sense of importance when I want to give *myself* a sense of importance. Do I make myself clear?

Unc. Mm. Like mud.

Penny. Why do you suppose I majored in Economics and Finance? To go into the stock market, of course.

Unc. To go into the . . . (*Controlling himself*) Very funny— very funny, but I'm not in a joking mood today.

Penny. It's not supposed to be funny. Unc, the way the world is nowadays you can't expect a woman to sit around and be a decoration until some man slips a Mrs. onto her name.

A PENNY SAVED

UNC. If you don't like sitting around you can go travelling, or get finished, or whatever it is young ladies of your set do.

PENNY. Finished is right. And I'm not a young lady of my set. You make it sound like something under glass.

UNC. Lots of girls wouldn't mind changing places with you.

PENNY. I know, and it isn't that I'm not grateful. But I couldn't be content being a parasite or a museum piece either. I've got a flair for finance. After all, that's natural. I'm Penny Brownell, niece of *Bearcat* Brownell, the shrewdest broker of the Exchange.

UNC. Never mind the flattery. The argument's closed. Come on; you can drive me home anyway.

PENNY. I haven't got the car—I've practically run all the way from Grand Central. And I won't budge until we get this thing settled.

UNC. You seem to have inherited the Brownell stubbornness—

PENNY. And the Brownell head, too. When other kids were brought up on Mother Goose I was reading the *Wall Street Journal*. I haven't watched you work for fifteen years for nothing.

UNC (*sarcastically*). I suppose you'd like to be a customer's man.

PENNY. That's it, Unc. Now you're talking. I've worked hard at college and I've studied world affairs, too. Besides, I've got my feminine intuition. Put me in one of your offices.

UNC. Kitten, I'm trying hard not to lose my temper. Did you ever hear of a customer's woman? A fine thing for my niece.

PENNY. Oh, I admit "Investment Counsel" sounds much better. But one can't expect to start at the top. Now in one of your smaller offices—

UNC. No. Definitely and absolutely no. You can't come near the market and that's final.

PENNY. Maybe it's final for you, Unc, but I bet one of your

competitors will be glad to hire me. Maybe Mr. Barkins—

UNC. Penny Brownell, if you try any monkey-shines—if you don't leave the Market strictly alone now and forever, I'll cut off your allowance. And you don't come into your grand-mother's money until you're twenty-one.

PENNY. That's fine. Then if I succeed without your help maybe you'll employ me after I've proven my worth.

UNC. I'll never employ you. (*Softening*) Look, Penny, don't you want to marry? I thought you and that Gordon boy were hitting it off pretty well.

PENNY. That stuffed shirt? The day I marry him apples will stay up in the air. Now I might consider some poor young man. One whose fortune I could make by my financial ad-vice— Unc, that's the solution to my idea.

UNC. Your idea?

PENNY. If I take some poor boy off the street and make him rich, well, reasonably rich—in say six months—will you give me a job?

UNC (*shouting*). No! Definitely and absolutely no.

PENNY. I'm glad you're open to conviction. (*Beginning to fade*) And now to find my man.

UNC (*shouting*). Penny Brownell, you come back. You stay away from strange men.

PENNY (*off mike*). Oh, Unc, from an expert that's an awfully old tip!

(*SOUND: Door closes with a bang.*)

(*MUSIC: Up and fade.*)

PENNY. . . . and that's why I'm sure I could be valuable to you, Mr. Barkins. All I want is a chance to show what I can do.

BARKINS (*oily voice*). Miss Brownell, I'd be delighted to employ you. I'm sure that with a knowledge of your Uncle's business and a desire to show him your ability, you'll stop at nothing to . . . well, I mean I'm sure we'll convince him of your talent. I always say it's good to have a member of the enemy camp—

PENNY (*interrupting indignantly*). If you're implying that I've come to sell out my uncle's inside information, you're crazy, Mr. Barkins. I don't know his business—I haven't been home from college long enough to learn it, and if I did know it, do you think I would sell it out to you? No, I asked for a chance to show him my own ability. I want to fight with my own brains—fairly and squarely. I can see that the Market needs honesty and the feminine touch. I'm sorry I came to the wrong place with them. Good day, Mr. Barkins.

(*SOUND: Door slams.*)

BARKINS (*laughing loudly*). Watta girl! Watta girl!

(*SOUND: Receiver off hook.*)

Get me Brownell!

(*SOUND: Phone rings.*)

Yes. Hello, Brownell. She was just here. I said what you told me to and boy she won't touch me with a ten foot pole. I wish I had a niece just like her.

(*MONTAGE—MUSIC: Up and down fast to sneak as background under the following scenes.*)

(*SOUND: Soda fountain noises.*)

PENNY (*fading in*). A small coke, please.

BOY. One coke, small.

PENNY. Young man, you look sort of intelligent.

BOY. Thanks, baby, you don't look so bad yourself, but I'm busy now.

PENNY. This is business. Would you like to make twenty-five thousand dollars?

BOY. Sure, and you're the queen of Sheba.

PENNY. Oh, not all for yourself, of course. But a ten per cent cut wouldn't be so bad.

BOY (*annoyed*). That would be just ducky. Look, Sister, I don't mind your having fun but I'm busy now—see? Here's your coke, and cool off. Hey, where's my nickel?

PENNY. Here, you'll need it. Opportunity has just passed you by.

(*MUSIC: Up and fade . . .*)

(*SOUND: Street noises. Taxi driving up.*)

DRIVER (*Irish*). Taxi, Miss?

PENNY. Yes.

(*SOUND: Door opens and shuts.*)

DRIVER. Where to, Miss?

PENNY. The Y.W. I want to get a room.—Oh no, *never mind*— I want to ride around— Go to Central Park.

DRIVER. Right.

(*SOUND: Cab starting.*)

PENNY. Tell me, Driver, are you married?

DRIVER. That I am. It'll be three months next Thursday.

PENNY. Do you make good money driving this cab?

DRIVER. It could be better and it could be worse. It won't be so bad when I get this cab paid for, and the weddin' paid up.

PENNY. Would you be interested in a proposition that could make you thousands of dollars overnight?

DRIVER (*indignantly*). Sure and I would not. Moider's out of me line, Miss. Besides, I'm goin' straight now. I promised Father Dougherty.

PENNY. But this is perfectly legitimate.

DRIVER. If some gang has put you up to this—

(*SOUND: Sudden putting on of brakes. Sudden Stop. Taxi door opens.*)

I suppose you're Mug Muggin's new moll. It's the devil's

trick and I've put the devil behind me. Yer can just git out o' me hack.

PENNY. Oh, Oh— I never was so insulted—

DRIVER. That may be, but I'm takin' no chances. You want to ride around, do you? You use the subway.

PENNY. You bet I will. You—you—oh!

(SOUND: *Taxi door slams. Footsteps downstairs. Sound of collision, things being dropped.*)

(MUSIC: *Background comes to a minor climax and cuts—on:*)

PENNY. Ouch! Oh, I'm sorry.

JIMMY. Yeah, well I guess no damage was done. Except darn it—I've got to add those figures all over again and I never get the same result twice.

PENNY. Do you fill these vending machines?

JIMMY. Yes. Isn't it a marvelous job? Say, I know you.

PENNY (*freezing*). I don't think so.

JIMMY. Sure I do. I never forget a face trimmed with blue eyes. The Brownell Building! I was filling the machine in the recreation room there and you and some Southern gal were eating apples and talking stock as if you meant it.

PENNY. I do. That was the telephone operator. But I don't remember seeing you.

JIMMY. Nobody sees me. I'm just part of the landscape. Let's see—29 and 7 is 36 and 9 is 46 and—

PENNY. Here, I'll do it. I've a head for figures. 36-45-54. There!

JIMMY. Imagine your having workable machinery beneath that gorgeous red hair! I suppose you think I'm pretty dumb. But I don't belong here—or do I! I'm doing this to humor a screwy uncle.

PENNY. Have you one of those? So have I.

JIMMY. I knew we had things in common. Mine wants me to learn the chewing gum business from the underground up.

So he sold me down the river to the vending company. What does yours want?

PENNY. Don't get me started on that. Well, goodbye, it was nice bumping into you.

JIMMY (*roaring*). A punster, no less. Don't you think you might tell me your name so when I fall for you again— See! Now *I'm* doing it.

(*They both laugh.*)

PENNY. Penelope Brownell.

JIMMY. You *have* got an uncle! I'm Jimmy Jenkins, named for the chewing gum king. He's mine! Look, suppose I knock off and we tear our uncles apart over some chocolate sodas.

PENNY. Can you play hookey?

JIMMY. You'd be surprised how good I am at it. Now when I was in college—

PENNY. Were you?

JIMMY. Oh sure, I'm a college man. Do you think I'd get this beautiful job if I weren't? Of course I'm going to work up. When they put vending machines in pent houses I'll be on the top.

PENNY. Say, maybe you're what I'm looking for.

JIMMY (*lightly*). I feel the same way about you.

PENNY. No, no, I've got a business proposition. Purely business. And if another man misunderstands, I'm licked.

JIMMY. Don't look like that. I was only kidding.

PENNY. You said you heard me talking about the stock market. Did I seem to know what I was talking about?

JIMMY. You fascinated me. Not that I understood half of it, but the Southern gal seemed to think you were quite the stuff.

PENNY. Will you behave if I have that soda with you?

A PENNY SAVED

JIMMY. Lady, you're safe with me. I'm from the Travellers' Aid. We meet all boats, planes and subway locals!—

(*MUSIC: Up and fade.*)

(*SOUND: Sound of glasses, etc.*)

PENNY. Mm. That was good.

JIMMY. As Omar said "A soda or two and thou in view—

PENNY (*warningly*). Jimmy—

JIMMY. "And business, too." What is it? I'm all ears.

PENNY. I'm afraid to tell you. I didn't do so well on my other prospects.

JIMMY. Why not? If you wanted to make them rich—

PENNY. Why, how did you know?

JIMMY. Oh I—I'm bright sometimes. I s'pose it was your Uncle being a Brownell and you knowing about the Market. I just put two and two together and in my usual fashion got six.

PENNY. It's the right answer this time. I'm trying to prove to Unc that I can be a broker.

JIMMY. Penelope, with eyes like that the only thing you'll break is hearts.

PENNY. Oh, so you've joined the rest.

JIMMY. Taboo, taboo. Sit down. I'll be good. When can I expect to make my first million?

PENNY. You mean you'll do it? You'll be my guinea pig?

JIMMY. Miss Brownell, you do say the sweetest things. What do I have to do?

PENNY. Just play the market according to my advice. Oh, but you'll have to give up your job.

JIMMY. That would be a pleasure if I could show my Uncle I could get along without him.

PENNY. You can, Jimmy. You'll get ten percent of all the profits

249

if there are profits, and there will be. And if there aren't, I'll give you a thousand dollars when I'm twenty-one and inherit some money from my grandmother.

JIMMY. How long will the job last?

PENNY. In times like these it will take at least six months. But if you're smart you'll learn enough about the Market to last a lifetime.

JIMMY (*dryly*). I wouldn't be surprised! It seeems like a very fair proposition to me. Where do we get the stake to start?

PENNY. Well, I've five hundred in the bank and I'm going to pawn my fur coat. I'll introduce you at one of Unc's offices and the account will stand in your name.

JIMMY. What happens if I run off with the money?

PENNY. You've got an honest face and I'll just have to take a chance. When I run the account up to where I want it, you'll get a statement showing all the transactions and I'll bring you and the statement to Unc.

JIMMY. As Exhibit A, huh?

PENNY. As Exhibit A. I'm going to take a room in New York to show Unc I really mean business.

JIMMY. Why not come over to my boarding house. Mrs. Gregory is Scotch—(*With a Scotch burr*) and a finer lassie you never saw on the heather. She's got a vacant room and you want to be close by to watch your investment, don't you?

PENNY. That's a marvelous idea. And Jimmy— It's my future I'm investing in, so don't run off, will you?

JIMMY. You've as slim a chance of losing me as the dimple in your cheek.

PENNY (*severely*). Jimmy, that's not Scotch—that's blarney and it's out.

JIMMY. Why, lady! That's just a small dividend from your investment.

A PENNY SAVED

(*MONTAGE—MUSIC: Up and down. Fast running under the following.*)

PENNY. We'll begin with a cheap oil stock on the Curb. Tell Smiley—

JIMMY (*on phone*). Hello, Smiley? James Jenkins, Jr. Oilex is fifty cents a share. Buy 1000 shares at ½. Right. B'ye.

(*SOUND: Hang up telephone.*)

(*MUSIC: Up and down.*)

PENNY. Railroads ought to be good now. Tell him—

JIMMY. Smiley? James Jenkins, Jr. Buy 300 shares of Great Southern at 1¼. Sell at 2. Right.

(*SOUND: Phone up.*)

(*MUSIC: Up and down.*)

PENNY. The international situation is rather critical now. The market is bound to react. Tell him—

JIMMY (*on phone*). James Jenkins, Jr. speaking. Sell 300 shares of United Airplane and sell an additional 200 short. Buy it back two points under. Right. (*To* PENNY) How do I know it's going down two points?

PENNY. You're bullish?

JIMMY (*into phone*). I'm foolish!

(*SOUND: Click of receiver on hook.*)

(*MUSIC: Cuts on phone.*)

JIMMY. Look, Penny. Ferdinand is tired. He wants to go out into the fields and kick up his heels a bit. What do you say we go to The Madrid and dance tonight?

PENNY. No. We've got reams of financial statements to study.

JIMMY. But, gosh, we've got to play once in a while.

PENNY. The Market is the only thing we can play just now.

JIMMY. But, Penny, you've doubled your money.

PENNY. It's not working fast enough. Now I think this candy company looks very—

JIMMY. Very sweet. I know. But you look sweeter.

PENNY. Ouch, that man's here again!

JIMMY. Penny, if you don't let me spend my commissions on you I'll do something desperate. I'll ball up your next deal.

PENNY. You wouldn't dare.

JIMMY. You don't know a Jenkins when he doesn't get his way!

PENNY. I'm beginning to. Jimmy, on the day your account reads $10,000 you can take me out in style. But until then the answer is "No." Definitely and absolutely no!

(*MUSIC: Up and fade.*)

(*SOUND: Phone rings.*)

JIMMY. Hello. Oh yes, Smiley. You think I handled that candy stock pretty neatly. How much profit? I thought you said twenty thousand dollars. (*Grandly*) Oh it's not tips, my boy, that gets me places. It's hard work. If you knew the hours I pored over financial statements— Ouch! (*Low*) Stop it, Penny. (*Into phone*) I was just kicked by a bull. A female bull.—Yes, I suppose that does make her a cow! Ouch! She's getting a bit restive. I'll let you know about the airplane stock tomorrow. 'Bye.

(*SOUND: Click of receiver on hook.*)

JIMMY. Well, imagine Smiley congratulating me on my shrewdness.

PENNY (*bitterly*). Don't you mean my shrewdness? You're actually beginning to believe you did it.

JIMMY (*on the serious side*). Oh, of course, not all of it.

PENNY. Of all the conceited, overbearing— Jimmy, what's come over you in the last few months? Has good luck gone to your head?

JIMMY. Look here, I resent your calling it luck. I've worked hard for everything we've gotten.

A PENNY SAVED

PENNY. You've worked hard! And what do you think I've been doing!—Jimmy, tell Smiley you want a statement of your account. The experiment's over. I think it's about time you met Uncle Pete.

(*MUSIC: Up and fade.*)

(*SOUND: Ticker—intermittent.*)

UNC. Well, Penny, I'm honored by this visit.

PENNY. Unc, you're going to have to admit defeat. Smiley says they're some of the shrewdest deals he's ever seen, and Mr. Jenkins has brought a statement showing every one of them.

UNC. Is that so? Where's the statement, Mr. Jenkins?

JIMMY (*blandly*). I'm afraid there isn't any.

PENNY. What do you mean? Didn't you get it from Smiley?

JIMMY. There isn't any because, well, my dear girl, I hate to disillusion you, but I've made off with your money.

PENNY. What are you talking about?

JIMMY. You see, that's my profession. Preying upon innocent women like yourself.

PENNY. I don't understand—

UNC. What's this?

JIMMY. At first I didn't think you were worth it because you didn't have any jewelry with you. But after all, your peculiar talent, shall we say, more than compensated for the loss.

UNC. Why, you blackguard! I'll call the police.

JIMMY. I wouldn't do that, Mr. Brownell, unless you want your niece's name all over the tabloids. She spent a lot of time alone with me.

PENNY. Why, we were—we were—we—

JIMMY. Of course she'll say we were studying financial statements, but what has she got to prove it?

UNC. This is blackmail!

253

JIMMY. Not exactly. You just agree to forget about the twenty thousand and your niece can put it down to experience.

PENNY (*breaking down*). Oh, this is awful. If you knew the things he told me.

UNC (*comforting her*). Never mind, kitten. Smarter women than you have fallen for scalawags.

PENNY (*indignantly*). Fallen for him? I haven't! (*Trailing off in tears*) Ooh, I can't believe it! I'm a flop. All I can do is marry that stupid Ted Gordon.

JIMMY. I hope he has a firm hand.

UNC (*bursting into laughter*). Stop it, Jimmy. I guess we made her say "uncle."

PENNY. Whhaat!

JIMMY. And let it be a lesson to you.

PENNY. Then you're not a blackmailer?

UNC. Are you disappointed? Jimmy's one of the smartest boys in my Philadelphia office. That's why I brought him in to check your deals.

PENNY (*enraged*). To check my—

UNC. Uh-huh. If he thought them wise he followed our instructions. And if he didn't he did just the opposite.

PENNY (*furious*). That's fine! That's swell! You didn't even give me a chance. Six months of my time living in a horrible furnished room, working like a dog, not having any fun— just to prove what a competent broker I am—and what do I get for it? A male guardian who makes Casanova look like an amateur.

UNC. What's this? What's this? Jimmy, that wasn't in the bond.

JIMMY. But I meant it.

PENNY. I suppose that was something Mr. Jenkins thought up to add an authentic touch.

A PENNY SAVED

JIMMY. Penny, you're not being fair.

PENNY. That sounds wonderful coming from you. Of all the unmitigated scoundrels— I suppose the chewing gum job and your uncle were made up, too.

JIMMY. I really have got a screwy uncle.

UNC. Now listen, Penny, you mustn't be too hard on Jimmy. He was only doing his job. I'm the guilty party.

PENNY. And you brag about it? Couldn't you at least have given me a fair chance?

UNC. And let you lose all your savings? I guess I had as much right to make a case as you had. It's a hard game. It only goes to show you that women haven't any business sense.

PENNY. If you had that statement you'd see how much business sense I had.

UNC. Of course you had some luck. Everyone does. But lately Jimmy's been reversing your orders—with my full knowledge and support, of course.

PENNY. And what is the latest order you reversed, Mr. Jenkins?

JIMMY. Oh, I did everything you told me until this week. After all, the technical condition of the market—

PENNY. So instead of buying you sold?

JIMMY. That's right. The railroad stock.

UNC. Really, Penny, you rely too much on your woman's intuition.

(*SOUND: Click of ticker.*)

PENNY. I suppose the ticker is woman's intuition, too.

UNC. What? Let me see that tape! By Jupiter, it's rising.

JIMMY. It couldn't be.

PENNY. Take a good look, Mr. Know-it-all.

UNC. $18\frac{1}{4}$—$\frac{1}{2}$—$18\frac{3}{4}$. It's turning over in huge blocks! 19—20. (*Shouting*) Jenkins!—I told you to use your judgment, but I took it for granted you had some.

255

JIMMY. But sir, you agreed with me. Why, you played the same way yourself.

UNC. What's that got to do with it? Don't you know a good tip when you hear one? Jenkins, you're fired!

PENNY (*triumphantly*). Well, Mr. Jenkins, your uncle must be screwier than mine is.

(*MUSIC: Up and fade.*)

(*SOUND: Sound of dishes. Paper rustling.*)

UNC. Aren't you going to eat your breakfast, honey?

PENNY. I'm not hungry.

UNC. Didn't you sleep well again?

PENNY. Oh sure, sure.

UNC. Look, Penny, there's no use moping around the house like a lost kitten. How was I to know you'd fall in love with Jimmy?

PENNY. I'm not in love with him. Please don't mention his name to me again.

UNC. All right. But here's a letter from him.

PENNY. What? How do you know?

UNC. Name's on the outside.

(*SOUND: Letter being torn open.*)

UNC. You dropped a check.

PENNY (*reading*). "Dear Penny; I thought you might like to know that while your uncle wouldn't let me follow your advice with your own money, I did, with my commissions, just to prove I had faith in you. So I am able to make up for the loss I caused you." (*Breaking off*). Unc, look at this!

UNC. (*reading*). "P. S. I have taken the chewing gum job—subway hours from nine to ten, and I have a thousand dollars in the bank you can invest for me. There's only one small detail. I'd like to marry my broker."—Well, Penny, you said something about wanting a poor man. But before you decide—there's a place for you in one of my offices, if you want it. Why, where are you rushing to?

PENNY. To the subway, to find my best client!

(*SOUND: Fade in on—ad lib subway rush background.*)

VOICES (*fades*).

1—(*W*) I says to Mrs. Flanagan, y've no right to be asking a respectable woman so much rent—and she says—

2—(*M*) The boss bawls me out all over the office and all's I did was spill the ink on his desk.

3—(*W*) Think what you're doing, Helen, before you tell him yes.

4—(*M*) (*loud*) Take it easy—you can't all get into this one train.

5—(*W*) I can't, can't I, well I'll show you.

4—(*M*) There'll be another Bronx express along in a minute— Get back away from the edge of the platform. . . .

(*SOUND: It synchronizes with the above VOICES to give the effect of trains getting started, etc. The train moves out of the station and there is a lull in the background.*)

JIMMY (*to himself*). I'm seein' gum in my sleep—and vending machines and pennies . . . 34 and 6 is 43 and 7 is 52—

PENNY (*off. Calls*). Jimmy—

JIMMY. Huh? Darn it! 34 and 6, 43 and 7—

PENNY. Jimmy!

(*FADES IN fast.*)

(*SOUND: Light footsteps and background up slightly.*)

PENNY. Jimmy (*She is out of breath.*)

JIMMY (*mad*). 34 and 6 is 43 and 7 is— HEY! Penny— (*Double take*) Penny!

PENNY. Yes— Don't stare at me. . . .

JIMMY (*he can hardly speak*). But, darling—I—I—I can't add up these darn figures.

257

A PENNY SAVED

PENNY. Silly, you never did have a head for figures.

JIMMY. Well, only yours— Darling— (*They go into a half clinch*) Gee—

PENNY. Gee—is right.

JIMMY. How nice you fit into my arms.

VOICE (*rushing past*). Would you mind standing off to the side of the platform?

JIMMY (*calls after him*). Sorry— (*To* PENNY) Am I forgiven?

(*SOUND: Train comes up fast and covers the next line.*)

PENNY. It wasn't your— (*From here on the line is covered. She shouts above it*)—I said it wasn't your fault.

JIMMY (*shouts. But the train has gone by*). What!—What DID YOU SAY— Oh, what did you say?

PENNY. It wasn't your fault.

JIMMY. Penny, darling! Did I forget to tell you today—(*Another train comes in fast—this time it is nearer*) THAT I LOVE YOU, PENNY?

PENNY. WHAT?

JIMMY. I LOVE YOU! (*The train has passed*) Darn it, I can't talk with all this competition—these subway trains have an annoying habit of punctuating my words . . . at the *wrong* places.

PENNY. What are you going to do? . . .

JIMMY. I've got it— Come on . . .

PENNY. Where to?

JIMMY. Come on. . . this telephone booth.

PENNY. Jimmy! That's wonderful . . .

JIMMY. It will be just a little quieter in here—

(*SOUND: Telephone booth door slides open.*)

JIMMY. Will you step into my office, Miss Brownell?

PENNY. How cozy, but it's a bit crowded, don't you think?

JIMMY. Not crowded—just—more intimate.

A PENNY SAVED

(*SOUND: Telephone booth door closes—background cuts.*)

JIMMY. Now—Miss Brownell, you were saying, in competition with some of the subway's loudest trains, that I was forgiven.

PENNY. Right. And that I'm going to marry you.

JIMMY. Huh?

PENNY. For your money, of course.

JIMMY. Oh, absolutely. If you don't run my pittance into a fortune, fast—we shall have to continue to live at Mrs. Gregory's High Class Boarding House and I shall have to continue with my subway activities.

PENNY. At least, I can always find you.

JIMMY. Yeah—but my uncle isn't so screwy after all. He delivered an ultimatum—said he'd promote me to the advertising department as soon as I had a wife—and no sooner.

PENNY. Well, darling, you're promoted to that advertising department, right now.

(*MUSIC: Up and to end.*)

Due